PERFORMANCE-BASED STANDARDS FOR CORRECTIONAL HEALTH CARE IN ADULT CORRECTIONAL INSTITUTIONS

First Edition

American Correctional Association

in cooperation with the Commission on Accreditation for Corrections

January 2002

American Correctional Association Staff

Hon. Betty Adams Green, President
James A. Gondles, Jr., CAE, Executive Director
Gabriella M. Daley, Director, Communications and Publications
Harry Wilhelm, Marketing Manager
Alice Fins, Publications Managing Editor
Michael Kelly, Associate Editor
Anne Hasselbrack, Editorial Assistant
Dana M. Murray, Graphics and Production Manager
Michael Selby, Graphics and Production Associate

Cover design by Michael Selby.

ISBN: 1-56991-150-9

Printed in the United States of America by Graphic Communications, Inc. Upper Marlboro, Maryland
Reprinted in 2016 by Gasch Printing, Odenton, Maryland

Information on accreditation may be obtained from:

American Correctional Association
Department of Standards and Accreditation
206 North Washington Street, Suite 200
Alexandria, VA 22314
(703) 224-0000

This publication may be ordered from:

American Correctional Association
206 North Washington Street, Suite 200
Alexandria, VA 22314
1-800-222-5646, ext. 0129

For information on publications and videos available from ACA, visit our website at www.aca.org.

CONTENTS

Part One: Continuum of Health Care Services

Part Two: Staff Training

Part Three: Offender Treatment

Part Four: Performance Improvement

Part Five: Offender Hygiene

Part Six: Safety and Sanitation

Part Seven: Administration

Appendices

Standards Manuals published by the American Correctional Association

2002 Standards Supplement
Standards for the Administration of Correctional Agencies
Performance-Based Standards for Adult Community Residential Services
Standards for Adult Correctional Boot Camp Programs
Standards for Adult Correctional Institutions
Standards for Adult Local Detention Facilities
Standards for Adult Parole Authorities
Standards for Adult Probation and Parole Field Services
Performance-Based Standards for Correctional Health Care in Adult Correctional Institutions
Standards for Correctional Industries
Standards for Correctional Training Academies
Standards for Electronic Monitoring Programs
Standards for Juvenile Community Residential Facilities
Standards for Juvenile Correctional Boot Camp Programs
Standards for Juvenile Day Treatment Programs
Standards for Juvenile Detention Facilities
Standards for Juvenile Probation and Aftercare Services
Standards for Juvenile Training Schools
Standards for Small Juvenile Detention Facilities
Standards for Small Jail Facilities
Certification Standards for Food Service Programs

These publications may be ordered from:

American Correctional Association
206 North Washington Street, Suite 200
Alexandria, VA 22314
1-800-222-5646, ext. 0129

Preface

Performance-Based Standards for Correctional Health Care in Adult Correctional Institutions is the second performance-based manual published by ACA. It is the first program offering an independent health care accreditation.

ACA published a precursor to this manual, *Certification Standards for Health Care Programs* in 1989. Designed as a stepping stone to full accreditation, it gave agencies the means to improve health care delivery and the opportunity to be recognized for their achievements.

Correctional health care has changed dramatically in the last decade and the Association recognized a need to update and improve health care standards. In 1999, ACA created a task force composed of health care and correctional professionals. Their mission was to develop contemporary health care standards in a performance-based model. Their goal was not only to create standards that ensure higher quality health care programs but also to give agencies a self-monitoring system that would give clinical and correctional managers usable information.

The first draft of *Performance-Based Standards for Correctional Health Care in Adult Correctional Institutions* was presented to the ACA Standards Committee in San Antonio, July 2000, and was approved for field testing. Field testing began with volunteer agencies in the fall of 2000 and after eight successful field tests, the task force reconvened in Lanham, Maryland in early summer of 2001 to review the results of the field tests. Revisions were made based upon the data received from the test sites, and the new document was released to a cross-section of correctional professionals for comment.

The field tests clearly established the reliability of the new standards and showed the significance of outcome measures in giving agencies an indispensable management tool. The Standards Committee approved the final revision in August of 2001 at the 131st Congress of Corrections in Philadelphia, Pennsylvania.

ACA continues its mission of improving practices in correctional facilities by helping agencies provide incarcerated populations with safe and effective health care.

Forewords

David L. Thomas, M.D., J.D.

Dr. Thomas is the Vice President of DCI, a professional consulting firm and the Director of Health Services for the Florida Department of Corrections. He is also a professor for Nova Southeastern College of Osteopathic Medicine, the Chairman of Nova's Division of Correctional Medicine and a Commissioner with the Commission on Accreditation.

Although the American Correctional Association has reviewed health care as a part of its auditing process there was awareness that a greater depth of involvement in correctional health care was an essential requirement for accredited facilities. To that end over many years, several eminent committees were formed, procedures thrashed out, qualifications discussed, approaches tackled, standards evaluated, and trials were performed. This volume is the work of that long period of labor.

The following standards are unique not only for correctional health care, but for the health care industry as well. This is the first large-scale comprehensive completed effort involving outcome measurement. The importance of a review predicated on *outcome measurements* cannot be underestimated.

Prior to this effort, accrediting agencies conducted evaluations for the presence or absence of an operation, condition, or situation. While that is an important function, it really gives no input to the effectiveness of the service. Outcome measurements evaluate the *consequences* of programs and activities rather than their presence or absence.

By analogy, the presence of a fire sprinkler system in a building is important. The fact that it works is essential. During most inspections, it is impossible to trigger the sprinkler system. However, due to its very nature, the delivery of health care lends itself well to direct testing. Each inmate cared for is a fire and each intervention for that inmate is a testing of the functioning of the sprinkler system.

For instance, in a long-term facility, patients with HIV ought to be treated. The presence or absence of that treatment is a measure of activity and is how previous accreditation was performed. Measuring the outcomes of that treatment gives the administration two separate parameters. First it affords an indication of the quality of the current care delivered. Second, by viewing the outcome measurements over time, trends can be readily ascertained. Evaluation of trends gives administrators real data upon which to base decisions.

By complying with the standards contained herein you will be on the cutting edge of the evaluation and accreditation process. I am personally pleased to have been a small part of the process. The ACA and facilities becoming accredited under these standards should be very proud of this work.

Harold W. Clarke

Commissioner Clarke began his career in corrections in 1974 and is currently the Director of the Nebraska Department of Correctional Services. He has been a member of ACA's Board of Governors and vice chair of its Ethics Committee as well as serving as an ACA auditor.

The provision of quality health care services to communities across the country is a challenging task. The task is especially difficult when the community exists within a correctional system. While diagnosis and treatment schedules may be similar, correctional agencies are forced to provide these services in unique and challenging environments.

Correctional systems are faced with providing health care services to a community, or population that tends to have many preexisting health conditions. Lifestyles, drug dependency issues, physical or mental health difficulties and the condition of confinement also impact the health of a correctional population. Delivering quality health care services in this environment distinctly differs from other health care settings.

One unequaled aspect of providing health care services in a correctional setting is that the program must be equally accessible for all who reside in the institution. While individualized treatment is provided, the process of service delivery must be the same. As a sole-source medical provider, correctional administrators will be well served by adopting the standards developed by the American Correctional Association. These standards not only will affirm that we are providing medical services, but they will provide us with a measurement of our efforts. This measurement will enable correctional agencies to benchmark their services and improve their quality of health care.

The standards developed are a clear indication that the correctional community is anxious to engage in a process which will identify deficiencies and weaknesses in the delivery of health care services or outputs and our outcomes. It is not enough to say that we provide health care services, but we must impact the health of our populations through these services. We need to know if quality medical services are being provided. These standards have been developed to meet the unique challenges facing corrections today. Correctional administrators now have a tool or model to assist them in providing quality health care services. Most of the individuals under our care and supervision will be returning to the communities at large. Left untreated or with ineffective health care, our task as a community is even more difficult. Therefore, it is imperative that we undertake this formidable and ambitious task to measure our effectiveness in providing health care to those under our supervision.

To meet this challenge, the process of delivering health care services must be evaluated within a correctional model. This model has been developed with much input from medical professionals outside the correctional environment. I am proud to be affiliated with a professional organization such as ACA, which is ready to assist us in meeting the unique challenges of providing quality health care to our populations and communities. These standards are an excellent model—a model that will continue to be developed and continuously improved much like all ACA standards. As with all ACA processes, this is a quest for continuous quality improvement, and you are encouraged to join in this journey.

Acknowledgments

We wish to extend our appreciation to all of the correctional professionals who have devoted a great deal of time and effort in making this manual a reality. *Performance-Based Standards For Correctional Health Care in Adult Correctional Institutions* embraces the Association's commitment to continuous quality improvement practices and represents the correctional community's dedication to excellence. We gratefully acknowledge all who offered comments, suggestions, and support during this project and we commend those who courageously piloted this program so effectively.

Major Contributors (in alphabetical order):

Kathleen Bachmier, RNC, MS, Director of Medical Services, North Dakota State Prison Division, Bismarck, North Dakota

Arleen Chin, RN, CNAA, Director of Nursing, Department of Corrections, Concord, New Hampshire

Jackie Ciolli, RN, Nursing Supervisor, Green Hill Training School, Chehalis, Washington

Rebecca Craig, RN, Director, Institute for Medical Quality, San Francisco, California

Gail Fricks, RN, Director of Medical Review, South Carolina Department of Corrections, Columbia, South Carolina

Elizabeth Gondles, Ph.D., President/CEO, Institute For Criminal Justice Healthcare, Alexandria, Virginia

Michael Hegmann, MD, Correctional Health Care Physician, Elayn Hunt Correctional Center, St. Gabriel, Louisiana

Robert Hofacre, MCRP, RN, Nursing Director, Ohio Department of Youth Services, Colubus, Ohio

Evalyn Horowitz, MD, Chief Medical Officer, Public Health Care Services, Department of Corrections, Sacramento, California

Harold S. Margolis, MD, Chief of Hepatitis Branch, Centers for Disease Control, Atlanta, Georgia

Susan Martin, Deputy Director, Department of Corrections, Medfield Massachusetts

Frederick R. Maue, MD, Chief, Clinical Services, Department of Corrections, Camp Hill, Pennyslvania

Jack McWay, Ph.D., Psychology Services, Federal Bureau of Prisons, Washington, DC

Kenneth Moritsugu, MD, Deputy Surgeon General, United States Office of Surgeon General, Rockville, Maryland

Dianne Rechtine, MD, Florida Department of Corrections, Orlando, Florida

Herbert A. Rosefield, Ed.D., Assistant Director Health Services, North Carolina Division of Prisons, Raleigh, North Carolina

Wayne Scott, Former Executive Director, Texas Department of Criminal Justice, Huntsville, Texas

Barbara Skeen, RN, Quality Assurance Manager, South Carolina Department of Corrections, Columbia, South Carolina

David L. Thomas, MD, JD, Director of Health Services, Department of Corrections, Tallahassee, Florida

Lester Wright, MD, Associate Commissioner, Chief Medical Officer, Department of Corrections, Albany, New York

COMMISSION ON ACCREDITATION FOR CORRECTIONS

Executive Committee

Geno Natalucci-Persichetti, Ohio, *Chair*
Mark Fitzgibbons, *Vice Chair*
Odie Washington, *Member-at-Large*
Margarette Ghee, *Member-at-Large*
Robert Garvey, *Member-at-Large*

Commissioners

David M. Bogard, J.D., New York
Lynn Branham, J.D., Illinois
Mel Brown, Ph.D., Texas
Dan Catley, Virginia
Arleen Chin, R.N., C.N.N.A., New Hampshire
Harold Clarke, Nebraska
Barbara Dooley, Tennessee
Michael Frawley, Missouri
Michael S. Hamden, Esq., South Carolina
William Hamilton, Ohio

Robert Hofacre, M.C.R.P., R.N., Ohio
Sharon Johnson-Rion, Tennessee
Jeannette Kinker, New Mexico
Frederick Maue, M.D., Pennsylvania
Thomas Scott, Florida
Ted Sexton, Alabama
David L. Thomas, M.D., J.D., Florida
Cheryl Townsend, Arizona
Lester Wright, M.D. New York
Michael Youngken, Kansas

Standards and Accreditation Staff

R. J. Verdeyen, Director
Diane Blemberg, Assistant Director
Melissa Mall, Regional Manager
Tricia Munley-Norris, Regional Manager
Cecil Patmon, Regional Manager
Christine Powers, Regional Manager
Tom Ruby, Regional Manager
Kathleen McKim, R.N., L.H.R.M., Administrator of Health Care Programs
Marie Londot, Standards Associate
Gilda Miler, Office Manager
Denise Gresham, Administrative Assistant
Michelle Alston, Administrative Assistant
Doris Peoples-Payton, Administrative Assistant

AMERICAN CORRECTIONAL ASSOCIATION 2000-2002

Introduction to Accreditation

ACA and the Commission on Accreditation for Corrections (CAC) are private, nonprofit organizations that administer the only national accreditation program for all components of adult and juvenile corrections. Their purpose is to promote improvement in the management of correctional agencies through the administration of a voluntary accreditation program and the ongoing development and revision of relevant, useful standards.

Accreditation, a process that began in 1978, involves approximately 80 percent of all state departments of corrections and youth services as active participants. Also included are programs and facilities operated by the Federal Bureau of Prisons, the U. S. Parole Commission, and the District of Columbia. For these agencies, the accreditation program offers the opportunity to evaluate their operations against national standards, remedy deficiencies, and upgrade the quality of correctional programs and services. The recognized benefits from such a process include improved management, a defense against lawsuits through documentation and the demonstration of a "good faith" effort to improve conditions of confinement, increased accountability and enhanced public credibility for administrative and line staff, a safer and more humane environment for personnel and offenders, and the establishment of measurable criteria for upgrading programs, personnel, and the physical plant on a continuing basis.

The timelines, requirements, and outcomes of the accreditation process are the same for a state or federal prison, training school, local detention facility, private halfway house or group home, probation and parole field service agency, or paroling authority. All programs and facilities sign a contract, pay an accreditation fee, conduct a self-evaluation, and have a standards compliance audit by trained ACA auditors before an accreditation decision is made by the Commission. Once accredited, all programs and facilities submit annual certification statements to ACA. Also, at ACA's expense and discretion, a monitoring visit may be conducted during the initial three-year accreditation period to ensure continued compliance with the appropriate standards.

Participation in the Accreditation Process

Invitations to participate in the accreditation process have been extended to all adult and juvenile agencies for which standards have been developed and published. Participating agencies include public and private agencies; federal, state, and local agencies; and United States and Canadian correctional agencies.

Accreditation activities are initiated voluntarily by correctional administrators. When an agency chooses to pursue accreditation, ACA staff will provide the agency with appropriate information and application materials. These include a contract, the applicable manual of standards, a policy and procedure manual, and an organization summary (narrative).

Eligibility Criteria

To be eligible for accreditation, an agency must be a part of a governmental or private entity or conform to the applicable federal, state, and local laws and regulations regarding corporate existence. The agency must: (1) hold under confinement pretrial or presentence adults or juveniles who are being held pending a hearing for unlawful activity; or (2) hold under confinement sentenced adult offenders convicted of criminal activity or juveniles adjudicated to confinement; or (3) supervise in the community sentenced adult or adjudicated juvenile offenders, including juveniles placed in residential settings; and (4) have a single administrative officer responsible for agency operations. It is this administrative officer who makes formal application for admission for accreditation.

It is ACA's policy that nonadjudicated juveniles should be served outside the juvenile correctional system. Training schools housing status offenders must remove them before the facility can be awarded accreditation. Detention facilities may house status offenders who have violated valid court orders by continued perpetration of status offenses. In such instances, the following conditions would apply: status offenders are separated by sight and sound from delinquent offenders; facility staff demonstrate attempts to mandate removal of all status offenders from detention centers; and special programs are developed for status offenders.

ACA does not prohibit community programs that house adjudicated juveniles with status offenders in nonsecure settings from participation in accreditation. However, ACA actively supports and requires exclusion of status offenders from the criminal and juvenile justice systems. Residential facilities and institutional programs that house adults and juveniles separated by sight and sound may become accredited. Individual cases may stipulate removal of juveniles before receiving an accreditation award.

Preaccreditation Assessment

Prior to signing an accreditation contract, an agency may request a preaccreditation assessment. The assessment requires an ACA auditor to visit the agency. The auditor will assess strengths and areas for improvement, measure readiness for application for accreditation, and identify steps required to achieve accreditation. A confidential, written report is provided to the agency to assist in making the decision to apply for accreditation.

Applicant Status

When the agency enters into the accreditation process, the administrator requests an information package from ACA. To confirm eligibility, determine appropriate fees, and schedule accreditation activities, the agency provides ACA with relevant narrative information through the organization summary. The Applicant Status begins when both the completed organization summary, which provides a written description of the facility/program, and the signed contract are returned to ACA. The Association will notify the agency of its acceptance into the accreditation process within fifteen days of the receipt of the necessary application materials. ACA will then assign a regional manager from the Standards and Accreditation Department as a permanent liaison to the agency. The agency will appoint an accreditation manager, who will be responsible for organizing and supervising agency resources and activities to achieve accreditation.

As defined in the contract, the fees for the accreditation period cover all services normally provided to an agency by ACA staff, auditors, and the Commission. The fees are determined during the application period and are included in the contract signed by the agency and ACA.

Correspondent Status

When the application is accepted, the agency enters into Correspondent Status. During this time, the agency conducts a self-assessment of its operations and completes a self-evaluation report, which specify the agency's level of standards compliance.

At the agency's request and expense, an on-site accreditation orientation for staff and/or a field consultation is scheduled. The object of the orientation is to prepare agency staff to complete the requirements of accreditation, including an understanding of self-evaluation activities, compilation of documentation, audit procedures, and standards interpretation. A field auditor provides information on accreditation policy and procedure, standards interpretations, and/or documentation requirements. Agency familiarity with standards and accreditation is the key factor in determining the need for these services.

The self-evaluation report includes a compliance tally, and an explanation for each standard believed to be non-compliant or not applicable. It must be submitted no later than six weeks prior to the proposed audit date.

Applicable Standards

The standards used for accreditation address services, programs, and operations essential to good correctional management, including administrative, staff, and fiscal controls, staff training and development, physical plant, safety and emergency procedures, sanitation, food service, rules and discipline, and a variety of subjects that comprise good correctional practice. These standards are under continual revision to reflect changing practice, current case law, new knowledge, and agency experience with their application. These changes are published by ACA in the *Standards Supplement*.

ACA policy addresses the impact of the standards revisions on agencies involved in accreditation. Agencies signing contracts after the date that a *Standards Supplement* is published are held accountable for all standards changes in that supplement. Agencies are not held accountable for changes made after the contract is signed. The agencies may choose to apply new changes to the standards that have been issued following the program's entry into accreditation. Agencies must notify ACA of their decision before conducting the standards compliance audit.

For accreditation purposes, any new architectural design, building, and/or renovation of the institution must be in accordance with the current standards manual at the time of the design, building, and/or renovation. In such cases, different standards would be applied to separate parts of the institution, respective according to these changes in the physical plant.

Standards Compliance Checklist

In completing a standards compliance checklist, the agency checks compliance, noncompliance, or not applicable for each standard. Checking compliance signifies complete compliance with the content of the standard/expected practice at all times and that the agency has documentation (primarily written) available to support compliance. A finding of noncompliance indicates that all or part of the requirements stated in the standard/expected practice have not been met. A not applicable response means that the standard/expected practice is clearly not relevant to the situation being audited. A written statement supporting nonapplicability of the standard/expected practice is required.

At this time, the agency may request a waiver for one or more standards/expected practices, provided that overall agency programming compensates for the lack of compliance. The waiver request must be accompanied by a clear explanation of the compensating conditions. The agency applies for a waiver only when the totality of conditions safeguard the life, health, and safety of offenders and staff. Waivers are not granted for standards/expected practices designated as mandatory and do not change the conclusion of noncompliance or the agency's compliance tally. When a waiver is requested during the self-evaluation phase, ACA staff renders a preliminary judgment. A final decision can be made only by the Commission during the accreditation hearing. Most waivers granted are for physical plant standards.

The Association requires that a self-evaluation report be completed by each applicant for accreditation. It is recommended that agencies entering into the accreditation process for the first time submit a written statement to ACA concerning their status at the completion of the evaluation. Information contained in this statement should include the percentage of compliance with mandatory and nonmandatory standards/expected practices; a list of not applicable standards/expected practices; and a list of noncompliant standards/expected practices and their deficiencies.

The compilation of written documentation requires the most time and effort during Correspondent Status. A separate documentation file, which explicitly shows compliance, is prepared for each standard/expected practice.

In order to request an audit, an agency must comply with 100 percent of the standards/expected practices designated as mandatory and 90 percent of the nonmandatory standards/expected practices.

Candidate Status

The agency enters into Candidate Status with ACA's acceptance of the self-evaluation report or agency certification of its completion. Candidate Status continues until the agency meets the required level of compliance, has been audited by a visiting committee composed of ACA auditors, and has been awarded or denied a three-year accreditation by the Commission. Candidate Status lasts up to twelve months.

The agency requests a standards compliance audit when the facility administrator believes the agency or facility has met or exceeded the compliance levels required for accreditation (100 percent mandatory; 90 percent nonmandatory).

Standards Compliance Audit

The agency's request for an audit is made six to eight weeks before the desired audit dates. The purpose of the audit is to have the visiting committee measure the agency's operation against the standards based on the documentation provided by the agency. A visiting committee completes the audit and prepares a visiting committee report for submission to the Commission. ACA designates a visiting committee chair to organize and supervise the committee's activities.

Prior to arrival at the audit site, each member of the visiting committee reviews the agency's descriptive narrative and any additional information that ACA may have provided, including pending litigation and court orders submitted by the agency and any inmate correspondence. The visiting committee chair makes audit assignments to each auditor. For example, one auditor may audit the administrative, fiscal, and personnel standards/expected practices, while another audits standards/expected practices for physical plant, sanitation, and security. Upon arrival, the visiting committee meets with the administrator, accreditation manager, and other appropriate staff to discuss the scope of the audit and the schedule of activities. This exchange of information provides for the development of an audit schedule that ensures the least amount of disruption to routine agency operation.

The exact amount of time required to complete the audit depends on agency size, the number of applicable standards/expected practices, additional facilities to be audited, and accessibility and organization of documentation. To hasten the audit, all documentation should be clearly referenced and located where the visiting committee is to work.

The accreditation manager's responsibilities include compiling and making accessible to all visiting committee members the standards compliance documentation and release of information forms for personnel and offender records. Also, staff should be notified beforehand to ensure that they are available to discuss specific issues or conduct tours of the facility for the visiting committee.

During the audit, the members of the visiting committee tour the facility, review documentation prepared for each standard/expected practice, and interview staff and offenders to make compliance decisions. The visiting committee reports its findings on the same compliance checklist used by the agency in preparing its self-evaluation report. All members of the visiting committee review all mandatory standards/expected practices, all areas of noncompliance and nonapplicability, with decisions made collectively. Final decisions on waivers can be approved only by the Commission at the time of the agency's accreditation hearing.

Interviewing staff members and offenders is an integral part of the audit. In addition to speaking with those who request an interview with the team, the members of the visiting committee select other individuals to interview and with whom to discuss issues. Interviews are voluntary and occur randomly throughout the audit, and those interviewed are ensured that their discussions are confidential.

In addition to auditing standards/expected practices documentation, auditors will evaluate the quality of life or conditions of confinement. An acceptable quality of life is necessary for an agency to be eligible for accreditation. Factors that the visiting committee consider include: the adequacy and quality of programs, activities, and services available to offenders and juveniles and their involvement; occurrences of disturbances, serious incidents, assaults, or violence, including their frequency and methods of dealing with them to ensure the safety of staff and offenders or juveniles; and overall physical conditions, including conditions of confinement, program space, and institutional maintenance related to sanitation, health, and safety.

At the conclusion of the audit, the visiting committee again meets with the administrator, the accreditation manager, and any others selected by the administrator to discuss the results of the audit. During this exit interview, the visiting committee reports the compliance tally and all findings of noncompliance and nonapplicability.

If the visiting committee finds that the agency is in noncompliance with one or more mandatory standards/expected practices or does not meet sufficient nonmandatory standards/expected practices compliance levels to be considered for accreditation, the chair advises the agency that an on-site supplemental audit may be required prior to scheduling an accreditation hearing. The agency is responsible for notifying ACA when the deficiencies have been corrected and a supplemental audit is desired. The agency bears the cost of the supplemental audit. An ACA auditor, often a member of the original visiting committee, returns to the agency to re-audit the appropriate standards/expected practices. The visiting committee report includes the written report from the supplemental audit.

The chair of the visiting committee then prepares and submits a copy of the visiting committee report to ACA staff within two weeks of the completion of the audit. ACA staff review the report for completeness, enters the data, and within thirty (30) days of the audit's completion, it is submitted to the agency administrator and other members of the visiting committee for concurrence. Upon receipt of the visiting committee report, the agency has seven days to submit its written response to the report to ACA staff and the chairperson of the visiting committee.

The Accreditation Hearing

The CAC is responsible for rendering accreditation decisions and is divided into accreditation panels authorized to render such decisions. Panels meet separately, or with a full board meeting, and are composed of three to five commissioners.

The agency is invited to have representation at the accreditation hearing. Unless circumstances dictate otherwise, a member of the visiting committee is not present; however, an ACA staff member does participate. At the accreditation hearing, the agency representative provides information about the agency, speaks in support of its appeal and/or waiver requests, and addresses concerns the panel may have with regards to the accreditation application.

After completing its review, the accreditation panel votes to award or deny accreditation, continue the agency in Candidate Status, or place an agency on probation. When an agency receives a three-year accreditation award, a certificate with the effective date of the award is presented to the agency representative.

The Commission may stipulate additional requirements for accreditation if, in its opinion, conditions exist in the facility or program that adversely affect the life, health, or safety of the staff, juveniles or offenders. These requests are specific regarding activities required and timeliness for their completion. The panel advises the agency representative of all changes at the time the accreditation decision is made.

ACA and the Commission may deny accreditation for insufficient standards/expected practices compliance, inadequate plans of action, or failure to meet other requirements as determined by the Commission, including, but not limited to, the conditions of confinement in a given facility. In not awarding accreditation, the Commission may extend an agency in Candidate Status for a specific period of time and for identified deficiencies, if in its judgment the agency is actively pursuing compliance. Those agencies denied accreditation, but not extended in Candidate Status, may reapply for accreditation after 180 days. The agency receives written notification of all decisions relative to its accreditation following the accreditation hearing.

Accredited Status

During the three-year accreditation period, ACA requires that accredited agencies submit annual certification statements confirming continued standards/expected practices compliance at levels necessary for accreditation. The report should include the agency's progress on completing plans of action and other significant events that may affect the accreditation award. In addition, ACA may require accredited agencies to submit written responses to public criticism, notoriety, or patterns of complaints about agency activity that suggest a failure to maintain standards/expected practices compliance. The Association, at its own expense and with advance notice, may conduct on-site monitoring visits to verify continued standards/expected practices compliance or conditions of confinement.

Reconsideration Process

The goal of ACA's accreditation process is to ensure the equity, fairness, and reliability of its decisions, particularly those that constitute either denial or revocation of Accredited Status. Therefore, an agency may request reconsideration of any denial or revocation of accreditation. However, the reasonableness of ACA's standards, criteria, and/or procedures for accreditation may not serve as the basis for reconsideration.

A reconsideration request is based on the grounds that the adverse decision is (1) arbitrary, erratic, or otherwise in substantial disregard of the criteria and/or procedures for accreditation as stated by ACA, (2) based on incorrect facts or an incorrect interpretation of facts, or (3) unsupported substantial evidence.

The agency submits a written request for reconsideration to ACA staff within thirty days of the adverse decision stating the basis for the request. The Commission's Executive Committee reviews the request and decides whether there is sufficient evidence to warrant a reconsideration hearing before the entire Commission. The agency is notified in writing of the Executive Committee's decision.

Revocation of Accreditation

An accredited agency that does not maintain the required levels of compliance throughout the three-year accreditation period, including continuous compliance with all mandatory standards/expected practices, may have its accreditation award revoked. The agency is notified of its deficiencies and given a specified amount of time to correct them. If the deficiencies continue, the Commission may place the agency on Probationary Status for an additional stated period of time and require documentation of compliance. Should the agency fail to correct the deficiencies, the Commission may revoke the agency's accreditation and request that the Accreditation Certificate be returned to ACA. An accredited agency that has had its accreditation revoked for reasons of noncompliance also may use the recon-sideration process.

Reaccreditation

To ensure continuous Accredited Status, accredited agencies should apply for reaccreditation approximately twelve months before the expiration of their current accreditation award. For detailed information on reaccreditation, consult your ACA regional manager.

The preceding information is provided as an overview of the accreditation process. Additional information on specific procedures and elements of the process is available from ACA's Standards and Accreditation Department.

Expected Practices Numbering System

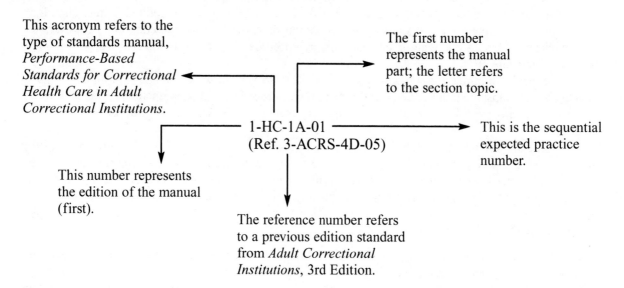

This acronym refers to the type of standards manual, *Performance-Based Standards for Correctional Health Care in Adult Correctional Institutions.*

The first number represents the manual part; the letter refers to the section topic.

1-HC-1A-01
(Ref. 3-ACRS-4D-05)

This is the sequential expected practice number.

This number represents the edition of the manual (first).

The reference number refers to a previous edition standard from *Adult Correctional Institutions*, 3rd Edition.

Summary of Mandatory Expected Practices

1-HC-1A-01	Access to Care
1-HC-1A-08	Emergency Plan
1-HC-1A-10	Pregnancy Management
1-HC-1A-11	Communicable Disease and Infection Control Program
1-HC-1A-13	Management of Hepatitis A, B, and C
1-HC-1A-14	Management of HIV Infection
1-HC-1A-15	Biohazardous Waste Management
1-HC-1A-16	Chronic Care
1-HC-1A-19	Health Screens for Inter-system Transfers
1-HC-1A-20	Health Screens for Intra-system Transfers
1-HC-1A-22	Health Appraisal
1-HC-1A-25	Mental Health Program
1-HC-1A-27	Mental Health Screens
1-HC-1A-28	Mental Health Appraisal
1-HC-1A-30	Suicide Prevention and Intervention
1-HC-1A-33	Detoxification
1-HC-1A-35	Pharmaceuticals
1-HC-2A-01	Health Authority
1-HC-2A-02	Provision of Treatment
1-HC-2A-03	Personnel Qualifications
1-HC-2A-05	Credentials
1-HC-2A-13	Emergency Plans
1-HC-2A-14	Emergency Response
1-HC-3A-03	Confidentiality
1-HC-3A-04	Informed Consent
1-HC-3A-07	Segregation
1-HC-3A-08	Involuntary Administration
1-HC-3A-09	Research
1-HC-3A-12	Use of Restraints
1-HC-4A-03	Quality Assurance
1-HC-4A-04	Peer review
1-HC-6A-02	Control of Instruments
1-HC-6A-04	Key Control
1-HC-6A-05	Annual Fire Inspection
1-HC-6A-06	Fire Codes and Regulations
1-HC-6A-07	Quarterly Fire Inspections
1-HC-6A-08	Fire Alarm
1-HC-6A-09	Evacuation Plan
1-HC-6A-10	Flammable, Toxic and Caustic Materials
1-HC-6A-11	Combustible Refuse
1-HC-6A-12	Facility Sanitation
1-HC-6A-13	Food Service Employees
1-HC-6A-14	Food Service Inspection

Performance-Based Standards for Correctional Health Care in Adult Correctional Institutions, First Edition

Totals of Weights

Category	Number
Mandatory Expected Pratices	43
Nonmandatory Expected Practices	80
Total	123

Dual Accreditation

Under existing guidelines, agencies have several options for accreditation.

• Facility accreditation
• Health care accreditation
• Dual accreditation

Dual accreditation provides agencies the opportunity to obtain accreditation awards for both the facility and the health care program using performance-based health care standards. If this option is chosen, the following expected practices will be reviewed as part of the facility audit.

1-HC-1A-37	1-HC-6A-12
1-HC-2A-12	1-HC-6A-13
1-HC-3A-15	1-HC-6A-14
1-HC-5A-01	1-HC-6A-15
1-HC-5A-02	1-HC-7A-04
1-HC-5A-03	1-HC-7A-07
1-HC-5A-05	1-HC-7B-01
1-HC-5A-07	1-HC-7B-02
1-HC-5A-08	1-HC-7B-03
1-HC-6A-03	1-HC-7B-04
1-HC-6A-04	1-HC-7B-05
1-HC-6A-05	1-HC-7B-06
1-HC-6A-07	1-HC-7B-07
1-HC-6A-08	1-HC-7C-01
1-HC-6A-09	1-HC-7C-02
1-HC-6A-10	1-HC-7C-03
1-HC-6A-11	

Total of Weights for Health Care with Dual Accreditation

Category	Number
Mandatory Expected Practices	32
Nonmandatory Expected Practices	57
Total	89

Performance-Based Standards Explained

This manual, *Performance-Based Standards for Correctional Health Care in Adult Correctional Institutions*, is the result of a new, major initiative undertaken by the American Correctional Association to improve the delivery of health care to offenders within the correctional environment using the concept and new template for performance based standards. Conceived and developed by health care professionals, these revised standards, practices, and outcome measures will enable administrators and practitioners to not only monitor health care activities but also to measure over time the outcomes of their efforts.

More than five years in the making, the American Correctional Association unveiled its first set of performance-based standards in August 2000. Partially funded by the Bureau of Justice Assistance (BJA), U.S. Department of Justice, *Performance-Based Standards for Adult Community Residential Services, Fourth Edition* is the prototype that will guide the eventual revision of all ACA standards' manuals.

I. The Basics

The Bottom Line—What's Different?

Table 1 describes the relationship between the elements of current standards and the new performance-based standards.

TABLE 1: Comparing the Elements of Performance-Based Standards With Previous ACA Standards and Accreditation Terms

NEW *Performance-Based* Element	Previous *Standards* Element
Standard	None (new element)
Outcome Measure	None (new element)
Expected Practice	**Standard**
Comment	**Comment**
Protocol	**Primary Documentation**
Process Indicator	**Secondary Documentation**

When Is a Standard No Longer a Standard?

As Table 1 suggests, the biggest *change* in terminology is that what we used to call "standards" all have been reclassified as "expected practices." The reason for this change reveals the fundamental difference between prior standards and ACA's new performance-based standards.

Without exception, the drafters of the new *Performance-Based Standards for Correctional Health Care in Adult Correctional Institutions* found that all prior health care standards described *activities or practices* that were prescribed for practitioners, but a performance-based standard should describe a *condition* to be achieved and maintained.

What Does This Mean for Accreditation?

Guided by a summary of significant incidents and a report that examines conditions of confinement, the Commission on Accreditation for Corrections currently examines issues that affect the life, health, and safety of staff and offenders. As data is collected for the new outcome measures, the Commission will have more information about actual and ongoing operations. More important, you will have an important new management tool.

II. The Fundamentals of Performance-Based Standards

ACA's performance-based standards are comprised of several elements:

- PERFORMANCE STANDARDS (as many as are needed to achieve the goal)
- OUTCOME MEASURES for each performance standard
- EXPECTED PRACTICES for each standard, and corresponding—
- PROTOCOLS, and
- PROCESS INDICATORS

These elements are defined and described in Table 2.

TABLE 2: Definitions of Terms for Performance-Based Standards

Element	Definition
Standard	A statement that clearly defines a required or essential *condition* to be achieved and maintained.
	A performance standard describes a "state of being," a condition, and does not describe the activities or practices that might be necessary to achieve compliance. Performance standards reflect the program's overall mission and purpose.
Outcome Measure	Measurable events, occurrences, conditions, behaviors or attitudes that demonstrate the extent to which the condition described in the performance standard has been achieved.
	Outcome measures describe the *consequences* of the program's activities, rather than describing the activities themselves.
	Outcome measures can be compared *over time* to indicate changes in the conditions that are sought. Outcome measure data are collected continuously but usually are analyzed periodically.

(continued)

TABLE 2:   Definitions of Performance-Based Standards (continued)

Element	Definition
Expected Practice(s)	Actions and activities that, if implemented properly (according to protocols), will produce the desired outcome. What we *think* is necessary to achieve and maintain compliance with the standard—but not necessarily the *only* way to do so. These are activities that represent the current experience of the field, but that are not necessarily supported by research. As the field learns and evolves, so will practices.
Protocol(s)	Written instructions that guide implementation of expected practices, such as: policies/procedures, post orders, training curriculum, formats to be used such as logs and forms, offender handbooks, diagrams such as fire exit plans, internal inspection forms.
Process Indicators	Documentation and other evidence that can be examined periodically and continuously to determine that *practices* are being implemented properly. These "tracks" or "footprints" allow supervisory and management staff to monitor ongoing operations.

The diagram on page xxvi (Table 3) attempts to describe the functional relationships among the elements.

TABLE 3: Functional Relationship of Performance-Based Standards Elements

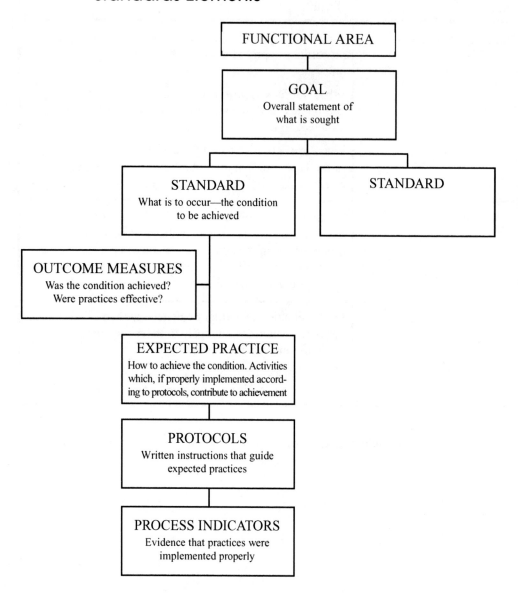

Each element is described and discussed in more detail in the following narrative.

PERFORMANCE STANDARD

A performance standard is a statement that clearly defines a required or essential *condition* to be achieved and maintained. A performance standard describes a "state of being," a condition, and does not describe the activities or practices that might be necessary to achieve compliance. Performance standards reflect the program's overall mission and purpose and contribute to the realization of the goal that has been articulated.

In the beginning, the drafters of the new standards found it difficult to articulate clear and concise standards. The closer a draft standard came to meeting the definition of a performance-based standard, the simpler it seemed to appear. In drafting the new performance-based standards, the committee was constantly fighting the urge to describe an *activity* rather than to identify the overarching purpose for the activity. During many of the working group meetings, it was common for a proposed standard to be met with the response "Why?" While often frustrating, by continuing to ask the "why" question, the drafters were able to identify the basic statements of conditions that must be defined through performance standards.

Because performance standards are so fundamental and basic, it is less likely that they will require frequent revision. But as the field continues to learn from experience, it is predicted, and even hoped, that the expected practices that are prescribed to achieve compliance with standards will continue to evolve.

OUTCOME MEASURES

Outcome measures are quantifiable (measurable) events, occurrences, conditions, behaviors, or attitudes that demonstrate the extent to which the condition described in the corresponding performance standard has been achieved. Outcome measures describe the *consequences* of the organization's activities, rather than describing the activities themselves.

Because outcome measures are quantifiable, they can be compared *over time* to indicate changes in the conditions that are sought. Measurable outcome data are collected continuously but are usually analyzed periodically. The first time you measure an outcome, you establish a point of reference. By comparing the next measurement (weeks or months later), you can identify progress, or lack of progress toward the desired outcome.

Outcome measures are distinct from the activities of a program. For example, counting the number of vaccinations given to inmates is not an outcome measure (it is a process indicator), but measuring the incidence of disease in the inmate population is an outcome measure. Giving vaccinations is an activity (practice) that we believe will improve inmate health (performance standard) that can be measured by the incidence of disease (outcome measure).

Similarly, the number of inmates who were provided with substance abuse treatment would be a process indicator, where the number of inmates who pass drug screening tests would be an outcome measure. Treatment activities (practices) are provided to reduce offender substance abuse (a performance standard), which can be measured by the results of drug tests (outcome measures).

Most performance standards have several outcome measures that may be used to determine if the condition described in the standard has been achieved. Conversely, a single outcome measure might be used to ascertain compliance for more than one standard. Outcome measures look at the bigger picture, by asking "what actually happened?"

EXPECTED PRACTICES

Expected practices are actions and activities that, if implemented properly (according to protocols), will produce the desired outcome—achievement of the condition described in the standard.

Expected practices represent what the practitioners *believe* is necessary to achieve and maintain compliance with the standard—but may not be the *only* way to achieve compliance. These activities represent the best thinking of the field, supported by experience, but often are not founded on research. As conditions change and as we learn from our experience, we expect practices to evolve.

It is arguable that expected practices *should* be changed over time to reflect our growing body of knowledge and experience. On the other hand, it is likely that we will see much less change with the overarching performance standards, which are more basic and fundamental.

PROTOCOLS

Protocols are written instructions and formats that guide implementation of expected practices, such as:

- policies and procedures
- post orders
- training curriculums

- formats to be used, such logs and forms
- diagrams such as fire exit plans
- internal inspection forms

Protocols provide a *map* to guide the proper implementation of expected practices. Protocols describe, usually in great detail, *how* to implement activities that are described in expected practices.

PROCESS INDICATORS

Process indicators can be used frequently—even continuously—to monitor activities and practices. But process indicators are not an "end" in and of themselves—they just tell if the expected practices are being implemented.

III. More About Outcome Measures and Process Indicators

Understanding the difference between outcome measures and process indicators can be difficult. *Process indicators relate directly to expected practices.* Process indicators tell you if practices are consistently implemented according to protocols. For example, several expected practices address the provision of substance abuse services to offenders. Process indicators can establish if measured activities—such as screening, assessment, and therapy—were actually delivered to offenders but it is the outcome measures, such as the results of drug tests, that determine whether offender substance abuse patterns were positively affected.

Most of the process indicators referenced in this draft refer to *written documentation* that can be consulted "after the fact." In addition to these "footprints" that are left by an organization, implementation of expected practices may be confirmed during on-site inspection activities such as observation or interviews (staff, volunteers, offenders, others.) Good managers combine review of documentation with random observation and interviews to monitor activities.

These additional activities (observations and interviews) are also a central part of ACA's accreditation process, comprising much of the work that is conducted on-site during audits. Accreditation participants also will recognize many of the protocols described in this draft as the "primary documentation" required by ACA as part of the accreditation process. Similarly, many of the process indicators cited in this draft are currently used as "secondary documentation" by the Commission on Accreditation for Corrections.

Observation and interview activities are usually suggested only when other methods are not possible and to verify the accuracy of documentation. Observation, interview, and measurement rely on an on-site "single point in time" activity, while the other methods have the ability to examine practices randomly, over a longer period of time.

Outcome measures look at the "bottom line." Was the desired condition or state of being described in the performance standard achieved?

There are three basic ways to express outcome measures:

- As **rates** (the frequency of an occurrence over time)
- As **ratios** (comparing two numbers as a fraction or decimal, such as the number of offenders diagnosed with hepatitis *divided by* the average daily population over the last twelve months) or
- As **proportions** (the relation of a part to the whole, such as the number of offender grievances found in favor of the offender *divided by* the total number of grievances filed). A percentage is a proportion multiplied by 100.

You rarely will find an outcome measure that calls for simply counting an event or occurrence. We believe that outcome measures should include a numerator *and* a denominator if they are to be useful as management tools.

Whenever possible, we have tried to use denominators that reflect the *volume* of activity. Therefore, it is preferable to divide by the average daily population rather than simply counting the number of events. We have tried to use the "Average Daily Population for the Past Twelve Months" whenever appropriate. In a few instances, we have used other denominators. A summary of the activities is contained in Appendix B of this manual entitled: "Health Care Outcome Measure Worksheet." For programs pursuing accreditation, the worksheet must be completed prior to an onsite evaluation of compliance.

What do the numbers mean after the math is done? They provide a *starting point* for analyzing and assessing the organization. The first time you generate outcome measures, they may not mean much to you, but their value grows every time you measure. The second time you measure outcomes, you will be able to compare current outcomes to those that you measured in the past. In this way, outcome measures become a valuable management tool. Over time, the series of outcome measures that you calculate can provide invaluable insight into many aspects of your operation. Sometimes, they will provide you with important "red flags" that identify troubling trends.

Using the new performance-based standards you can improve your organization by directing and managing activities better and by using outcome measures to evaluate if you achieved the desired results.

I. Continuum of Health Care Services

GOAL: Provide appropriate and necessary health services and care for offenders.

PERFORMANCE STANDARD

1A. **Offenders have unimpeded access to a continuum of health care services so that their health care needs, including prevention and health education, are met in a timely and efficient manner.**

OUTCOME MEASURES:

(1) Number of offenders with a positive tuberculin skin test on admission in the past twelve months divided by the annual number of admissions.

(2) Number of offenders diagnosed with active tuberculosis in the past twelve months divided by the average daily population in the past twelve months.

(3) Number of conversions to a positive tuberculin skin test in the past twelve months divided by the number of tuberculin skin tests given in the past twelve months.

(4) Number of offenders with a positive tuberculin skin test who complete prophylaxis treatment for tuberculosis in the past twelve months divided by the number of offenders with a positive tuberculin skin test on prophylaxis treatment for tuberculosis in the past twelve months.

(5) Number of Hepatitis C positive offenders in the past twelve months divided by the average daily population in the past twelve months.

(6) Number of HIV positive offenders in the past twelve months divided by the average daily population in the past twelve months.

(7) Number of HIV positive offenders who are being treated with highly active antiretroviral treatment in the past twelve months divided by the number of known HIV positive offenders in the past twelve months.

(8) Number of offenders diagnosed with an Axis I (excluding sole diagnosis of substance abuse) in the past twelve months divided by the average daily population in the past twelve months.

(9) Number of offender suicide attempts in the past twelve months divided by the average daily population in the past twelve months.

(10) Number of offender suicides in the past twelve months divided by the average daily population in the past twelve months.

(11) Number of offender deaths due to homicide in the past twelve months divided by the average daily population in the past twelve months.

(12) Number of offender deaths due to injuries in the past twelve months divided by the average daily population in the past twelve months.

(13) Number of medically expected offender deaths in the past twelve months divided by the average daily population in the past twelve months.

(14) Number of medically unexpected offender deaths in the past twelve months divided by the average daily population in the past twelve months.

(15) Number of offender admissions to the infirmary (where available) in the past twelve months divided by the average daily population in the past twelve months.

(16) Number of offender admissions to off-site hospitals in the past twelve months divided by the average daily population in the past twelve months.

(17) Number of offenders transported off-site (via an ambulance or correctional vehicle) for treatment of emergency health conditions in the past twelve months divided by the average daily population in the past twelve months.

(18) Number of offender speciality consults completed in the past twelve months divided by the number of specialty consults (on-site or off-site) ordered by primary health care provider (MD, NP, PA) in the past twelve months.

(19) Number of offender grievances about access to health care services found in favor of the offender in the past twelve months divided by the number of offender grievances about access to healthcare services in the past twelve months.

(20) Number of offender grievances related to the quality of health care found in favor of offenders during a twelve-month period divided by the number of offender grievances related to the quality of health care during a twelve-month period.

(21) Number of offender grievances related to unfair treatment or rights violation found in favor of offenders during a twelve-month period divided by the number of offender grievances related to unfair treatment or rights violation during the past twelve-months.

(22) Number of offender grievances related to safety or sanitation found in favor of offenders during a twelve-month period divided by the number of offender grievances related to safety or sanitation during the past twelve-months.

(23) Number of offenders' lawsuits about access to healthcare services found in favor of offenders in the past twelve months divided by the number of offenders' lawsuits about access to healthcare services in the past twelve months.

(24) Number of individual sick call encounters in the past twelve months divided by the average daily population in the past twelve months.

(25) Number of physician contacts in the past twelve months divided by the average daily population.

(26) Number of individualized dental treatment plans in the past twelve months divided by the average daily population in the past twelve months.

(27) Number of hypertensive offenders enrolled in a chronic care clinic in the past twelve months divided by the average daily population in the past twelve months.

(28) Number of diabetic offenders enrolled in a chronic care clinic in the past twelve months divided by the average daily population in the past twelve months.

(29) Number of incidents involving pharmaceuticals as contraband in the past twelve months divided by the average daily population in the past twelve months.

(30) Number of cardiac diets received by offenders with cardiac disease in the past twelve months divided by the number of cardiac diets prescribed in the past twelve months.

(31) Number of hypertensive diets received by offenders with hypertension in the past twelve months divided by the number of hypertensive diets prescribed in the past twelve months.

(32) Number of diabetic diets received by offenders with diabetes in the past twelve months divided by the number of diabetic diets prescribed in the past twelve months.

(33) Number of renal diets received by offenders with renal disease in the past twelve months divided by the number of renal diets prescribed in the past twelve months.

(34) Number of needle-stick injuries in the past twelve months divided by the number of employees in the past twelve months.

(35) Number of pharmacy dispensing errors in the past twelve months divided by the number of prescriptions dispensed by the pharmacy in the past twelve months.

(36) Number of nursing medication administration errors in the past twelve months divided by the number of medications administered in the past twelve months.

EXPECTED PRACTICES

Access to Care

1-HC-1A-01
(Ref. 3-4331)

(MANDATORY) Upon arrival at the facility, all offenders are informed about how to access health services and the grievance system. This information is communicated orally and in writing, and is conveyed in a language that is easily understood by each offender.

Comment: No member of the correctional staff should approve or disapprove offender's requests for health care services. The facility should follow the policy of explaining access procedures orally to offenders unable to read. When the facility frequently has non-English speaking offenders, procedures should be explained and written in their language.

Protocols: Written policy divided by procedures. An offender handbook. Grievance procedure.
Process Indicators: Documentation that offenders are informed about health care and grievance system. Offender grievances. Interviews.

1-HC-1A-02
Ref. (New)

When medical copayment fees are imposed, the program ensures that, at a minimum, the following are observed:

- *all offenders are advised, in writing, at the time of admission to the facility of the guidelines of the copayment program*
- *needed offender health care is not denied due to lack of available funds*
- *copayment fees shall be waived when appointments or services, including follow-up appointments, are initiated by medical staff*

Comment: Offenders should receive appropriate health care based on need, without regard to financial status. Fees imposed should not be so excessive as to discourage offenders from seeking needed medical care.

Protocols: Written policy and procedure.
Process Indicators: Forms. An offender handbook. Interviews. Financial records.

Clinical Services

1-HC-1A-03
(Ref. 3-4353)

There is a process for all offenders to initiate requests for health services on a daily basis. These requests are triaged daily by health professionals or health trained personnel. A priority system is used to schedule clinical services. Clinical services are available to offenders in a clinical setting at least five days a week and are performed by a physician or other qualified health care professional.

<u>Comment</u>: A priority system addresses routine, urgent, and emergent complaints and conditions. Health care request forms must be readily available to all offenders.

<u>Protocols</u>: Written policy and procedure. Sick call request form.
<u>Process Indicators</u>: A health record. Sick call request forms. Clinical provider schedules. Observation. Interviews.

Continuity of Care

1-HC-1A-04
(Ref. 3-4330)

Continuity of care is required from admission to transfer or discharge from the facility, including referral to community-based providers, when indicated.

<u>Comment</u>: When health care is transferred to providers in the community, appropriate information should be shared with the new providers in accordance with consent requirements.

<u>Protocols</u>: Written policy and procedure. Referral transfer form.
<u>Process Indicators</u>: Completed referral transfer forms. Health records. Facility logs. Interviews.

Referrals

1-HC-1A-05
(Ref. 3-4360)

Offenders who need health care beyond the resources available in the facility, as determined by the responsible physician, are transferred under appropriate security provisions to a facility where such care is on call or available twenty-four hours per day. A written list of referral sources includes emergency and routine care. The list is reviewed and updated annually.

<u>Comment</u>: Treatment of an offender's condition should not be limited by the resources and services available within a facility. Health care staff should collaborate with security personnel in determining conditions of transportation and necessary security precautions when an offender needs to be transported to another facility or provider.

<u>Protocols</u>: Written policy and procedure. Referral consult form.
<u>Process Indicators</u>: Health records. Completed referral consult records. Documentation of annual list review. Transportation logs. Interviews.

Transportation

1-HC-1A-06
(Ref. New)

A transportation system that assures timely access to services that are only available outside the correctional facility is required. Such a system needs to address the following issues:

- *prioritization of medical need*
- *urgency (for example, an ambulance versus a standard transport)*
- *use of a medical escort to accompany security staff*
- *transfer of medical information*

The safe and timely transportation of offenders for medical, mental health, and dental clinic appointments, both inside and outside the correctional facility (for example, to the hospital, health care provider, or another correctional facility) is the joint responsibility of the facility or program administrator and the health services administrator.

<u>Comment</u>: It is essential that the medical and the custody staff work cooperatively in the design and implementation of the medical transport system. Consideration should balance issues of security as well as medical or psychological concerns about the use of restraint devices that may affect the offender's health condition or access to care.

<u>Protocols</u>: Written policy or procedure. Transport form, log.
<u>Process Indicators</u>: Health records. Completed transport forms and log entries. Observations. Interviews.

Treatment Plan

1-HC-1A-07
(Ref. 3-4355)

A written treatment plan is required for offenders requiring close medical supervision, including chronic and convalescent care. This plan includes directions to health care and other personnel regarding their roles in the care and supervision of the patient, and is approved by the appropriate licensed physician, dentist, or mental health practitioner for each offender requiring a treatment plan.

<u>Comment</u>: Offenders requiring treatment plans include the following: the chronically ill, offenders with serious communicable diseases, the physically disabled, pregnant offenders, the terminally ill, offenders with serious mental health needs, and the developmentally disabled.

<u>Protocols</u>: Policy or procedure. Treatment plan format.
<u>Process Indicators</u>: Health records. Interviews.

Emergency Plan

1-HC-1A-08
(Ref. 3-4350)

(MANDATORY) There is a written plan for twenty-four-hour emergency medical, dental, and mental health services availability. The plan includes the following:

- *on-site emergency first aid and crisis intervention*
- *emergency evacuation of the offender from the facility*

- *use of an emergency medical vehicle*
- *use of one or more designated hospital emergency rooms or other appropriate health facilities*
- *emergency on-call or available twenty-four hours per day, physician, dentist, and mental health professional services when the emergency health facility is not located in a nearby community*
- *security procedures providing for the immediate transfer of offenders, when appropriate*

Comment: In the event that primary health services are not available, and particularly in emergency situations, back-up facilities or providers should be predetermined. The plan may include the use of an alternative hospital emergency service or a physician on-call service.

Protocols: Written policy or procedure.

Process Indicators: Designated facility. Provider lists. Transportation logs. Interviews.

Infirmary Care

1-HC-1A-09
(Ref. 3-4354)

Offenders are provided access to infirmary care. If infirmary care is provided onsite, it includes, at a minimum, the following:

- *definition of the scope of infirmary care services available*
- *a physician on call or available twenty-four hours per day*
- *health care personnel have access to a physician or a registered nurse and are on duty twenty-four hours per day when patients are present*
- *all offenders/patients are within sight or sound of a staff member*
- *an infirmary care manual that includes nursing care procedures*
- *an infirmary record that is a separate and distinct section of the complete medical record*
- *compliance with applicable state statutes and local licensing requirements.*

Comment: An infirmary is a specific area of a health care facility, separate from other housing areas, where offenders are housed and provided health care. Admission and discharge from this area is controlled by medical orders or protocols.

Protocols: Written policy or procedures. Nursing manual. Licensing requirements and regulations.

Process Indicators: Admission and inpatient records. Staffing schedules. Documentation of compliance with licensing requirements and regulations. Observations. Interviews.

Pregnancy Management

1-HC-1A-10
(Ref. 3-4343-1)

(MANDATORY) If female offenders are housed, access to pregnancy management services is available. Provisions of pregnancy management include the following:

- *pregnancy testing*
- *routine and high-risk prenatal care*

- *management of chemically addicted pregnant offenders*
- *comprehensive counseling and assistance*
- *appropriate nutrition*
- *postpartum follow up*

<u>Comment</u>: Management should include family planning services prior to release.
<u>Protocols</u>: Written policy and procedure. Offender handbook. Contract or agreement.
<u>Process Indicators</u>: Health record entries. Laboratory records. Interviews.

Communicable Disease and Infection Control Program

1-HC-1A-11
(Ref. 3-4366)

(MANDATORY) There is a written plan to address the management of infectious and communicable diseases. The plan includes procedures for prevention, education, identification, surveillance, immunization (when applicable), treatment, follow-up, isolation (when indicated), and reporting requirements to applicable local, state, and federal agencies. A multidisciplinary team that includes clinical, security, and administrative representatives, meets at least quarterly to review and discuss communicable disease and infection control activities.

<u>Comment</u>: Because of their serious nature, methods of transmission, and public sensitivity, these diseases require special attention. Agencies should work with the responsible public health authority in establishing policy and procedure that include the following: an ongoing education program for staff and offenders; control, treatment, and prevention strategies, which may include screening and testing, special supervision, or special housing arrangements, as appropriate; protection of individual confidentiality; and media relations.

<u>Protocols</u>: Written policy and procedure. Treatment guidelines.
<u>Process Indicators</u>: Health records. Laboratory, x-ray reports, and logs. Chronic care forms and clinic visit logs. Minutes of communicable disease and infection control committee meetings. Interviews.

1-HC-1A-12
(Ref. 3-4365)

There is a written plan to address the management of tuberculosis. The plan includes procedures for initial and ongoing testing for infection, surveillance, treatment (including treatment of latent tuberculosis), follow-up, and isolation (when indicated).

<u>Comment</u>: Plans for the management of tuberculosis may be based on incidence and prevalence of the disease within the agency's population and the surrounding community.

<u>Protocols</u>: Written policy and procedure. Treatment guidelines.
<u>Process Indicators</u>: Health records. Laboratory, x-ray reports and logs. Chronic care forms and clinic visit logs. Minutes of communicable disease and infection control committee meetings. Interviews.

1-HC-1A-13
(Ref. New)

(MANDATORY) There is a written plan to address the management of hepatitis A, B, and C. The plan includes procedures for the identification,

surveillance, immunization (when applicable), treatment (when indicated), follow-up, and isolation (when indicated).

<u>Comment</u>: None.

<u>Protocols</u>: Written policy and procedure. Treatment guidelines.
<u>Process Indicators</u>: Health records. Laboratory reports, x-ray reports, and logs. Chronic care forms and clinic visit logs. Minutes of communicable disease and infection control committee meetings. Interviews.

1-HC-1A-14
(Ref. New)

(MANDATORY) There is a written plan to address the management of HIV infection. The plan includes procedures for the identification, surveillance, immunization (when applicable), treatment, follow-up, and isolation (when indicated).

<u>Comment</u>: None.

<u>Protocols</u>: Written policy and procedure. Treatment guidelines.
<u>Process Indicators</u>: Health records. Laboratory reports, x-ray reports, and logs. Chronic care forms and clinic visit logs. Minutes of communicable disease and infection control committee meetings. Interviews.

1-HC-1A-15
(Ref. New)

(Mandatory) There is a plan for the management of biohazardous waste and for the decontamination of medical and dental equipment.

<u>Comment</u>: None.

<u>Protocols</u>: Written policy, procedure, codes, and regulations.
<u>Process Indicators</u>: Documentation of waste pick up, spore count logs, and/or cleaning logs.

Chronic Care

1-HC-1A-16
(Ref. New)

(MANDATORY) There is a plan for the treatment of offenders with chronic conditions such as hypertension, diabetes, and other diseases that require periodic care and treatment. The plan must address the monitoring of medications, laboratory testing, the use of chronic care clinics, health record forms, and the frequency of specialist consultation and review.

<u>Comment</u>: Professionally recognized chronic care guidelines are available from disease-specific organizations and various medical and physician associations.

<u>Protocols</u>: Written policy and procedure. Chronic care protocols and forms.
<u>Process Indicators</u>: Health records. Chronic care logs. Specialist schedules.

Dental Care

1-HC-1A-17
(Ref. 3-4347)

Routine and emergency dental care is provided to each offender under the direction and supervision of a licensed dentist. There is a defined scope of available dental services, including emergency dental care, which includes the following:

- *dental screening conducted within seven days of admission, unless completed within the last six months*
- *a full dental examination by a dentist and instruction on oral hygiene*
- *preventive care by dentally trained personnel within three months of admission, diagnostic x-rays are to be taken if necessary*
- *a defined charting system is completed that identifies the oral health condition and specifies the priorities for treatment by category*
- *development of an individualized treatment plan for each offender receiving dental care*
- *consultation and referral to dental specialists, including oral surgery, is provided, when necessary*

Comment: The dental examination should include taking or reviewing the offender's dental history and a full examination of hard and soft tissue of the oral cavity; diagnostic x-rays should be available, if deemed necessary. The examination results should be recorded on a uniform dental record. Oral hygiene and preventive care instruction may include the use of videotaped material.

Protocols: Written policy and procedure. Dental screening by examination forms. Dental care request forms.

Process Indicators: Dental records. Admission logs. Referral and consultation records. Dental request forms. Dental interviews.

Health Education

1-HC-1A-18
(Ref. 3-4363)

An ongoing program of health education and wellness information is provided to all offenders.

Comment: Health education and wellness topics may include but are not to be limited to information on access to health care services, dangers of self-medication, personal hygiene and dental care, prevention of communicable diseases, substance abuse, smoking cessation, family planning, self-care for chronic conditions, self-examination, and the benefits of physical fitness.

Protocols: Written policy and procedure.
Process Indicators: Documentation of program availability. Program and class schedules. Attendance rosters. Interviews. Curriculum and lesson plans. Examples of pamphlets, brochures, or other written handouts.

Health Screens

1-HC-1A-19
(Ref. 3-4343)

(MANDATORY) Intake medical screening for offender transfers, excluding intrasystem, commences upon the offender's arrival at the facility and is performed by health-trained or qualified health care personnel. All findings are recorded on a screening form approved by the health authority. The screening includes at least the following:

Inquiry into:
- *any past history of serious infectious or communicable illness, and any treatment or symptoms (for example, a chronic cough, hemoptysis,*

lethargy, weakness, weight loss, loss of appetite, fever, night sweats that are suggestive of such illness), and medications
- *current illness and health problems, including communicable diseases*
- *dental problems*
- *use of alcohol and other drugs, including type(s) of drugs used, mode of use, amounts used, frequency used, date or time of last use, and history of any problems that may have occurred after ceasing use (for example, convulsions)*
- *the possibility of pregnancy and history of problems (female only); and other health problems designated by the responsible physician*

Observation of the following:
- *behavior, including state of consciousness, mental status, appearance, conduct, tremor, and sweating*
- *body deformities, ease of movement, and so forth*
- *condition of the skin, including trauma markings, bruises, lesions, jaundice, rashes, infestations, recent tattoos, and needle marks or other indications of drug abuse*

Medical disposition of the offender:
- *general population*
- *general population with prompt referral to appropriate health care service*
- *referral to appropriate health care service for emergency treatment*

Offenders who are unconscious, semiconscious, bleeding, or otherwise obviously in need of immediate medical attention, are referred. When they are referred to an emergency department, their admission or return to the facility is predicated on written medical clearance. When screening is conducted by trained custody staff, procedures will require a subsequent review of positive findings by the licensed health care staff. Written procedures and screening protocols are established by the responsible physician in cooperation with the facility manager.

Comment: Health screening is a system of structured inquiry and observation to (1) prevent newly arrived offenders who pose a health or safety threat to themselves or others from being admitted to the general population, and to (2) identify offenders who require immediate medical attention.

Receiving screening can be performed at the time of admission by health care personnel or by a health trained correctional officer. Facilities that have reception and diagnostic units or a holding room must conduct receiving screening on all offenders on their arrival at the facility as part of the admission procedures.

Protocols: Written policy and procedure. Screening forms.
Process Indicators: Health records. Completed screening forms. Transfer logs. Interviews.

1-HC-1A-20
(Ref. 3-4344)

(MANDATORY) All intrasystem transfer offenders receive a health screening by health-trained or qualified health care personnel which commences on their arrival at the facility. All findings are recorded on a screening form approved by the health authority. At a minimum, the screening includes the following:

Inquiry into:
- *whether the offender is being treated for a medical or dental problem*
- *whether the offender is presently on medication*
- *whether the offender has a current medical or dental complaint*

Observation of:
- *general appearance and behavior*
- *physical deformities,*
- *evidence of abuse or trauma*

Medical disposition of offenders:
- *to general population*
- *to general population with appropriate referral to health care service*
- *referral to appropriate health care service for service for emergency treatment*

Comment: Health screening of intrasystem transfers is necessary to detect offenders who pose a health or safety threat to themselves or others and who may require immediate health care.

Protocols: Written policy and procedure. Screening form.

Process Indicators: Health records. Completed screening forms. Transfer logs. Interviews.

1-HC-1A-21
(Ref. New)

All in-transit offenders receive a health screening by health-trained or qualified health care personnel on entry into the agency system. Findings are recorded on a screening form that will accompany the offender to all subsequent facilities until the offender reaches his or her final destination. Health screens will be reviewed at each facility by health-trained or qualified health care personnel. Procedures will be in place for continuity of care.

Comment: None.

Protocols: Written policy and procedure.

Process Indicators: Health records. Completed screening forms. Transfer logs. Interviews.

Health Appraisal

1-HC-1A-22
(Ref. 3-4345)

(MANDATORY) A comprehensive health appraisal for each offender, excluding intrasystem transfers, is completed as defined below, after arrival at the facility. If there is documented evidence of a health appraisal within the previous ninety days, a new health appraisal is not required, except as determined by the designated health authority. Health appraisals include the following:

Within fourteen days after arrival at the facility
- *review of the earlier receiving screen*
- *collection of additional data to complete the medical dental, mental health, and immunization histories*
- *laboratory or diagnostic tests to detect communicable disease, including venereal disease and tuberculosis*

- *record of height, weight, pulse, blood pressure, and temperature*
- *other tests and examinations, as appropriate*

Within fourteen days after arrival for inmates with identified significant health care problems

- *medical examination, including review of mental and dental status (for those inmates with significant health problems discovered on earlier screening such as cardiac problems, diabetes, communicable diseases, and so forth)*
- *review of the results of the medical examination, tests, and identification of problems by a physician or other qualified health care personnel, if such is authorized in the medical practice act*
- *initiation of therapy, when appropriate*
- *development and implementation of a treatment plan, including recommendations concerning housing, job assignment, and program participation*

Within thirty days after arrival for inmates without significant health care problems

- *medical examination, including review of mental and dental status (for those inmates without significant health care concerns identified during earlier screening–no identified acute or chronic disease, no identified communicable disease, and so forth)*
- *review of the results of the medical examination, tests, and identification of problems by a physician or other qualified health care professional, if such is authorized in the medical practice act*
- *initiation of therapy, when appropriate*
- *development and implementation of a treatment plan, including recommendations concerning housing, job assignment, and program participation*

Comment: Test results, particularly for communicable diseases, should be received and evaluated before an offender is assigned to housing in the general population. Information regarding the offender's physical and mental status may also dictate housing and activity assignments. When appropriate, additional investigation should be conducted into alcohol and drug abuse and other related problems.

Protocols: Written policy and procedure. Health appraisal form.
Process Indicators: Health records. Completed health appraisal forms. Transfer logs. Interviews.

1-HC-1A-23
(Ref. 3-4346)

Health appraisal data collection and recording will include the following:

- *a uniform process as determined by the health authority*
- *health history and vital signs collected by health-trained or qualified health care personnel*
- *collection of all other health appraisal data performed only by qualified health personnel*
- *review of the results of the medical examination, tests, and identification of problems is performed by a physician or mid-level practitioner, as allowed by law*

Comment: None.

Protocols: Written policy and procedure.
Process Indicators: Health records.

Periodic Examinations

1-HC-1A-24
(Ref. 3-4348)

The conditions for periodic health examinations for offenders are determined by the health authority.

Comment: All offenders should receive a thorough physical examination. All offenders should be examined prior to release to protect both the offender and the public.

Protocols: Written policy and procedure.
Process Indicators: Health records. Completed annual health appraisal forms. Interviews.

Mental Health Program

1-HC-1A-25
(Ref. 3-4336)

(MANDATORY) There is a mental health program that includes at a minimum:

- *screening for mental health problems on intake as approved by the mental health professional*
- *outpatient services for the detection, diagnosis, and treatment of mental illness*
- *crisis intervention and the management of acute psychiatric episodes*
- *stabilization of the mentally ill and the prevention of psychiatric deterioration in the correctional setting*
- *elective therapy services and preventive treatment where resources permit*
- *provision for referral and admission to licensed mental health facilities for offenders whose psychiatric needs exceed the treatment capability of the facility*
- *procedures for obtaining and documenting informed consent*

Comment: An adequate number of qualified staff members should be available to deal directly with offenders who have severe mental health problems and to advise other correctional staff about their contacts with such individuals.

Protocols: Written policy and procedure. Screening form.
Process Indicators: Health records. Completed screening forms. Provider qualifications and time and attendance records. Observations. Interviews.

1-HC-1A-26
(Ref. 3-4337)

The mental health program is approved by the appropriate mental health authority and provides for all activities carried out by mental health services personnel.

Comment: None.

Protocols: Written policy and procedure. Job descriptions for mental health personnel.
Process Indicators: Documentation of review by mental health personnel. Interviews.

Mental Health Screen

1-HC-1A-27
(Ref. New)

(MANDATORY) All intersystem and intrasystem transfer offenders will receive an initial mental health screening at the time of admission to the facility by mental health trained or qualified mental health care personnel. The mental health screening includes, but is not limited to:

Inquiry into:
- *whether the offender has a present suicide ideation*
- *whether the offender has a history of suicidal behavior*
- *whether the offender is presently prescribed psychotropic medication*
- *whether the offender has a current mental health complaint*
- *whether the offenders are being treated for mental health problems*
- *whether the offender has a history of inpatient and outpatient psychiatric treatment*
- *whether the offender has a history of treatment for substance abuse*

Observation of:
- *general appearance and behavior*
- *evidence of abuse and/or trauma*
- *current symptoms of psychosis, depression, anxiety, and/or aggression*

Disposition of offender:
- *to the general population*
- *to the general population with appropriate referral to mental health care service*
- *referral to appropriate mental health care service for emergency treatment*

Comment: None.

Protocols: Written policy and procedure. Mental health screening form.
Process Indicators: Health records. Completed mental health screening forms. Transfer logs. Interviews.

Mental Health Appraisal

1-HC-1A-28
(Ref. New)

(MANDATORY) All intersystem offender transfers will undergo a mental health appraisal by a qualified mental health person within fourteen days of admission to a facility. If there is documented evidence of a mental health appraisal within the previous ninety days, a new mental health appraisal is not required, except as determined by the designated mental health authority. Mental health examinations include, but are not limited to:

- *assessment of current mental status and condition*
- *assessment of current suicidal potential and person-specific circumstances that increase suicide potential*
- *assessment of violence potential and person-specific circumstances that increase violence potential*
- *review of available historical records of inpatient and outpatient psychiatric treatment*

- *review of history of treatment with psychotropic medication*
- *review of history of psychotherapy, psycho educational groups, and classes or support groups*
- *review of history of drug and alcohol treatment*
- *review of educational history*
- *review of history of sexual abuse-victimization and predatory behavior*
- *assessment of drug and alcohol abuse and/or addiction*
- *use of additional assessment tools, as indicated*
- *referral to treatment, as indicated*
- *development and implementation of a treatment plan, including recommendations concerning housing, job assignment, and program participation*

Comment: None.

Protocols: Written policy and procedure. Mental health appraisal form. *Process Indicators*: Health records. Completed mental health appraisal forms. Transfer logs. Interviews.

Mental Health Evaluations

1-HC-1A-29
(Ref. 3-4349)

Offenders referred for mental health treatment will receive a comprehensive evaluation by a licensed mental health professional. The evaluation is to be completed within fourteen days of the referral request date and include at least the following:

- *review of mental health screening and appraisal data*
- *direct observations of behavior*
- *collection and review of additional data from individual diagnostic interviews and tests assessing personality, intellect, and coping abilities*
- *compilation of the individual's mental health history*
- *development of an overall treatment/management plan with appropriate referral to include transfer to mental health facility for offenders whose psychiatric needs exceed the treatment capability of the facility*

Comment: Comprehensive individual psychological evaluations should be performed when there is a reasonable expectation that such evaluation will serve a therapeutic or disposition function useful to the overall interests of the offender. Written reports describing the results of the assessment should be prepared and all information should be appropriately filed.

Protocols: Written policy and procedure. Mental health referral form.
Process Indicators: Health records. Completed referral forms. Interviews with mental health provider(s). Clinic visit records.

Suicide Prevention and Intervention

1-HC-1A-30
(Ref. 3-4364)

(MANDATORY) There is a written suicide prevention plan that is approved by the health authority and reviewed by the facility or program administrator. The plan includes staff and offender critical incident debriefing that covers the management of suicidal incidents, suicide watch, and death of an offender or staff member. It ensures a review of critical incidents by administration, security, and health services. All staff with responsibility for offender

supervision are trained on an annual basis in the implementation of the program. Training should include but not be limited to:

- *identifying the warning signs and symptoms of impending suicidal behavior*
- *understanding the demographic and cultural parameters of suicidal behavior, including incidence and variations in precipitating factors*
- *responding to suicidal and depressed offenders*
- *communication between correctional and health care personnel*
- *referral procedures*
- *housing observation and suicide watch level procedures*
- *follow-up monitoring of offenders who make a suicide attempt*

<u>Comment</u>: The program should include specific procedures for handling intake, screening, identifying, and supervising of a suicide-prone offender and be signed and reviewed annually.

<u>Protocols</u>: Written policy and procedures. Training curriculum and lesson plans. Suicide watch logs or forms.

<u>Process Indicators</u>: Health records. Documentation of staff training. Documentation of suicide watches and critical incident debriefings. Observations. Interviews.

Mental Illness and Developmental Disability

1-HC-1A-31
(Ref. 3-4367)

Offenders with severe mental illness or who are severely developmentally disabled receive a mental health evaluation and, where appropriate, are referred for placement in noncorrectional facilities or in units specifically designated for handling this type of individual.

<u>Comment</u>: Offenders with severe mental illness or developmental disabilities are vulnerable to abuse by other offenders and require specialized care. These individuals may be a danger to themselves or others or be incapable of attending to their basic physiological needs.

<u>Protocols</u>: Written policy and procedures.
<u>Process Indicators</u>: Health records. Referral logs. Records. Interviews.

Prostheses and Orthodontic Devices

1-HC-1A-32
(Ref. 3-4358)

Medical or dental adaptive devices (eyeglasses, hearing aids, dentures, wheelchairs, or other prosthetic devices) are provided when the health of the offender would otherwise be adversely affected, as determined by the responsible physician or dentist.

<u>Comment</u>: Offenders may be required to provide copayments for these devices.
<u>Protocols</u>: Written policy and procedure.
<u>Process Indicators</u>: Purchase records. Health records. Interviews.

Detoxification

1-HC-1A-33
(Ref. 3-4370)

(MANDATORY) Detoxification is done only under medical supervision in accordance with local, state, and federal laws. Detoxification from alcohol, opiates, hypnotics, other stimulants, and sedative hypnotic drugs is conducted under medical supervision when performed at the facility or is conducted in a hospital or community detoxification center. Specific guidelines are followed for the treatment and observation of individuals manifesting mild or moderate symptoms of intoxication or withdrawal from alcohol and other drugs. Offenders experiencing severe, life-threatening intoxication (an overdose) or withdrawal are transferred under appropriate security conditions to a facility where specialized care is available.

<u>Comment</u>: None.

<u>Protocols</u>: Written policy and procedure. Community contract agreements.
<u>Process Indicators</u>: Health records. Transfer records. Interviews.

Management of Chemical Dependency

1-HC-1A-34
(Ref. 3-4371)

Offenders have access to a chemical dependency treatment program. When a chemical dependency program exists, the clinical management of chemically dependent offenders includes at a minimum the following:

- *a standardized diagnostic needs assessment administered to determine the extent of use, abuse, dependency, and/or codependency*
- *an individualized treatment plan developed and implemented by a multidisciplinary clinical team that includes medical, mental health, and substance abuse professionals*
- *prerelease relapse-prevention education, including risk management*
- *the offender will be involved in aftercare discharge plans*

<u>Comment</u>: None.

<u>Protocols</u>: Written policy and procedure.
<u>Process Indicators</u>: Health records. Interviews. Prerelease, preventive or education curriculum.

Pharmaceuticals

1-HC-1A-35
(Ref. 3-4341)

(MANDATORY) Proper management of pharmaceuticals includes the following provisions:

- *a formulary is available*
- *a formalized process for obtaining nonformulary medications*
- *prescription practices, including requirements that*
    - *(1) medications are prescribed only when clinically indicated as one facet of a program of therapy*
    - *(2) a prescribing provider reevaluates a prescription prior to its renewal*
- *procedures for medication procurement, receipt, distribution, storage, dispensing, administration, and disposal*

- *secure storage and perpetual inventory of all controlled substances, syringes, and needles*
- *the proper management of pharmaceuticals is administered in accordance with state and federal law*
- *administration of medication by persons properly trained and under the supervision of the health authority and facility or program administrator or designee*
- *accountability for administering or distributing medications in a timely manner and according to physician orders*

Comment: The formulary should include all prescription and nonprescription medications stocked in a facility or routinely procured from outside sources. Controlled substances are those classified by the Drug Enforcement Agency as Schedule II-V. The pharmacy should be managed by a pharmacist or health-trained personnel approved by the health authority.

Protocols: Written policy and procedure. Federal and state laws and regulations. Format for documentation of medication, inventory, and storage of medication.
Process Indicators: Health records. Completed medication administration, inventory, and storage forms. Documentation of compliance with federal and state laws.

Nonprescription Medication

1-HC-1A-36
(Ref. New)

If offenders have access to nonprescription (over-the-counter) medications that are available outside of health services, the items, the policy, and procedures are approved jointly by the facility or program administrator and the health authority.

Comment: Approved medications may be purchased through the commissary or the canteen.

Protocols: Written policy or procedure.
Process Indicators: Commissary or canteen items. Documentation of health authority approval. Interviews.

Dietary Allowances

1-HC-1A-37
(Ref. 3-4297)

(MANDATORY) The facility's dietary allowances are reviewed at least annually by a qualified nutritionist or dietician to ensure that they meet the nationally recommended dietary allowances for basic nutrition for appropriate age groups. Menu evaluations are conducted at least quarterly by food service supervisory staff to verify adherence to the established basic daily servings.

Comment: Copies of menu evaluations should be forwarded to the health authority.

Protocols: Written policy and procedure. Recommended dietary allowances.
Process Indicators: Annual reviews. Nutritionist or dietician qualifications. Documentation of at least annual review and quarterly menu evaluations. Interviews.

Therapeutic Diets

1-HC-1A-38
(Ref. 3-4299)

Therapeutic diets are provided as prescribed by appropriate clinicians. A therapeutic diet manual is available in the health services and food services areas for reference and information.

Comment: Therapeutic diets are prepared and served to offenders according to the orders of the treating clinician or as directed by the responsible health authority official. Prescriptions for therapeutic diets should be specific and complete, furnished in writing to the food service manager, and rewritten quarterly. Therapeutic diets should be kept as simple as possible and should conform as closely as possible to the foods served other offenders.

Protocols: Written policy and procedures. Diet manual. Diet request form.
Process Indicators: Health records. Diet records or forms. Observation. Interviews.

II. Staff Training

PERFORMANCE STANDARD

2A. **The provision of health services should be done in a professionally acceptable manner including the requirement that all staff be adequately trained and qualified and can demonstrate competency in their assigned duties.**

OUTCOME MEASURES:

(1) Number of staff with lapsed licensure and/or certification during the past twelve-month period divided by the number of licensed or certified staff during the past twelve-month period.

(2) Number of new employees during the past twelve-month period who completed orientation training prior to undertaking job assignments divided by the number of new employees during the past twelve-month period.

(3) Number of employees completing in-service training requirements in the past twelve months divided by the number of employees eligible in the past twelve months.

(4) Number of staff turnover per position category (MD, RN, LPN, medical records, and so forth) during the past twelve-month period divided by the number of staff positions per category during the past twelve months.

(5) Number of staff terminations for violation of drug-free work policy during the past twelve-month period divided by the number of staff terminations during the past twelve-month period.

EXPECTED PRACTICES
Health Authority

1-HC-2A-01
(Ref. 3-4326)

(MANDATORY) The facility has a designated health authority with responsibility for ongoing health care services pursuant to a written agreement, contract, or job description. Such responsibilities include the following:

- *establishing a mission statement that defines the scope of health care services*
- *developing mechanisms, including written agreements, when necessary, to assure that the scope of services is provided and properly monitored*
- *developing a facility's operational health policies and procedures*
- *identifying the type of health care providers needed to provide the determined scope of services*
- *establishing systems for the coordination of care among multidisciplinary health care providers*
- *developing a quality management program*

The health authority may be a physician, health services administrator, or health agency. When the health authority is other than a physician, final clinical judgments rest with a single, designated, responsible physician. The health authority is authorized and responsible for making decisions about the deployment of health resources and the day-to-day operations of the health services program.

<u>Comment</u>: The health authority and health services administrator may be the same person. The responsibility of the health authority includes arranging for all levels of health services, assuring the quality of all health services, and assuring that offenders have access to them. Health services provides for the physical and mental well-being of the offender population and should include medical and dental services, mental health services, nursing care, personal hygiene, dietary services, health education, and attending to environmental conditions. While overall responsibility may be assumed at the central office level, it is essential that each facility have an on-site health services administrator. The health authority and health services administrator may be the same person.

<u>Protocols</u>: Written policy and procedure. Sample agreement or contract requirements. Job description.

<u>Process Indicators</u>: Documentation of health authority designation. Contract. Billing records. Interviews. Documentation of mission statement, operational policies and procedures, scope of services and required personnel, coordination of care, and a quality management program.

Provision of Treatment

1-HC-2A-02
(Ref. 3-4327)

(MANDATORY) Clinical decisions are the sole province of the responsible clinician and are not countermanded by nonclinicians.

<u>Comment</u>: The provision of health care is a joint effort of administrators and health care providers and can be achieved only through mutual trust and cooperation. The health authority arranges for the availability of health care services; the responsible clinician determines what services are needed; the official responsible for the facility provides the administrative support for making the services accessible to offenders.

<u>Protocols</u>: Written policy and procedure.
<u>Process Indicators</u>: Health record entries. Offender grievances. Interviews.

Personnel Qualifications

1-HC-2A-03
(Ref. New)

(MANDATORY) If the facility provides health care services, they are provided by qualified health care personnel whose duties and responsibilities are governed by written job descriptions that are on file in the facility and are approved by the health authority. If offenders are treated at the facility by health care personnel other than a licensed provider, the care is provided pursuant to written standing or direct orders by personnel authorized by law to give such orders.

<u>Comment</u>: Job descriptions should include qualifications and specific duties and responsibilities. Verification consists of copies of credentials or a letter

confirming credential status from state licensing or certification body. Standing medical orders are for the definitive treatment of identified conditions and for the on-site emergency treatment of any person having such condition. Direct orders are those written specifically for the treatment of one person's particular condition.

Protocols: Written policy and procedures. Job descriptions. Standing orders.
Process Indicators: Verification of credentials or licensure. Documentation of compliance with standing orders. Health record entries. Interviews.

1-HC-2A-04
(Ref. 3-4338)

When institutions do not have full-time, qualified health care personnel, a health trained staff member coordinates the health delivery services in the institution under the joint supervision of the responsible health authority and warden or superintendent.

Comment: The health-trained staff member (who is other than a nurse, mid-level practitioner, or emergency medical technician) may be full-time or part-time. Coordination duties may include reviewing receiving screening forms for needed follow-up, readying offenders and their records for sick call, and assisting in carrying out orders regarding such matters as diets, housing, and work assignments.

Protocols: Written policy and procedures. Job description for health-trained personnel.
Process Indicators: Health records. Observation. Interviews.

Credentials

1-HC-2A-05
(Ref. 3-4334)

(MANDATORY) All professional staff comply with applicable state and federal licensure, certification, or registration requirements. Verification of current credentials and job descriptions are on file in the facility.

Comment: None.

Protocols: Written policy and procedure. Copies of licensure requirements.
Process Indicators: Personnel records. Documentation of licensure, certification, or registration. Documentation of current credentials.

Employee Orientation

1-HC-2A-06
(Ref. 3-4079)

All new full-time employees must complete a formalized, forty-hour orientation program before undertaking their assignments. At a minimum, the orientation program should include instruction in the following: the purpose, goals, policies, and procedures for the facility and parent agency; security and contraband regulations; key control; appropriate conduct with offenders; responsibilities and rights of employees; universal precautions; occupational exposure; personal protective equipment; biohazardous waste disposal; and an overview of the correctional field.

Comment: None.

Protocols: Written policy and procedure. A curriculum or lesson plan.
Process Indicators: Documentation of staff completion. Training records. Interviews.

1-HC-2A-07
(Ref. 3-4085)

All part-time staff and contract personnel receive a formal orientation appropriate to their assignments and additional training, as needed.

Comment: Part-time staff should receive orientation to institutional rules, security, and operational issues.

Protocols: Written policy and procedure. A curriculum or lesson plan.
Process Indicators: Documentation of staff completion. Training interviews. Interviews.

1-HC-2A-08
(Ref. 3-4082)

All health care staff who have offender contact receive forty hours of training in addition to orientation training during their first year of employment and forty hours of training each year thereafter.

Comment: None.

Protocols: Written policy and procedure.
Process Indicators: Training records. Interviews.

Employee Health

1-HC-2A-09
(Ref. New)

All new direct care staff receive a test for tuberculosis prior to job assignment and ongoing testing thereafter.

Comment: None.

Protocols: Written policy and procedure.
Process Indicators: Employee records. Interviews.

1-HC-2A-10
(Ref. New)

All direct care staff are offered the hepatitis B vaccine series.

Comment: None.

Protocols: Written policy and procedure.
Process Indicators: Employment records. Interviews.

Rules and Regulations

1-HC-2A-11
(Ref. New)

Staff acknowledge, in writing, that they have reviewed facility work rules and regulations, ethical standards, conditions of employment, and related documents.

Comment: None.

Protocols: Written policy and procedure. Work rules, ethics, and regulations that are posted, distributed, and disseminated.
Process Indicators: Documentation of review by employees.

Drug-free Workplace

1-HC-2A-12
(Ref. 3-4061)

The facility implements a drug-free workplace policy. Policies specify support for a drug-free workplace and are reviewed annually and include, at a minimum, the following:

- *prohibition of the use of illegal drugs*
- *prohibition of possession of any illegal drug, except in the performance of official duties*
- *procedures to be used to ensure compliance*
- *opportunities available for treatment and/or counseling for drug abuse*
- *penalties for violation of the policy*

<u>Comment</u>: None.

<u>Protocols</u>: Written policy and procedures. Drug-free workplace plan.
<u>Process Indicators</u>: Documentation of annual review of the plan.

Emergency Plans

1-HC-2A-13
(Ref. 3-4208)

(MANDATORY) All health care personnel delivering health care in the facility are trained in the implementation of the facility's emergency plans. Health care personnel are included in facility emergency drills, as applicable.

<u>Comment</u>: Emergency plans include those for fire, natural disaster, power outage, hostage situation, riot, and other disturbances.

<u>Protocols</u>: Written policy and procedure. Facility-plan specifications. A schedule for drills.
<u>Process Indicators</u>: Documentation of drills. Facility logs. Interviews.

Emergency Response

1-HC-2A-14
(Ref. 3-4351)

(MANDATORY) Correctional and health care personnel are trained to respond to health-related situations within a four-minute response time. The training program is conducted on an annual basis and is established by the responsible health authority in cooperation with the facility or program administrator and includes instruction on the following:

- *recognition of signs and symptoms, and knowledge of action that is required in potential emergency situations*
- *administration of basic first aid*
- *certification in cardiopulmonary resuscitation (CPR) in accordance with the recommendations of the certifying health organization*
- *methods of obtaining assistance*
- *signs and symptoms of mental illness, violent behavior, and acute chemical intoxication and withdrawal*
- *procedures for patient transfers to appropriate medical facilities or health care providers*
- *suicide intervention*

Comment: The facility administrator or designee may designate those correctional officers and health care providers who have responsibility to respond to health care emergencies. Staff not physically able to perform CPR are exempt from the expected practice.

Protocols: Written policy and procedure. Lesson plans and curriculum.
Process Indicators: Verification of training. Records and certificates. Interviews.

First Aid

1-HC-2A-15
(Ref. 3-4352)

First aid kits are available in designated areas of the facility based on need.

Comment: The availability and placement of first aid kits are determined by the designated health authority in conjunction with the facility administrator. The health authority approves the contents, number, location, and procedures for monthly inspection of the kit(s) and develops written procedures for the use of the kits by nonmedical staff.

Protocols: Written policy and procedure.
Process Indicators: List of first aid kit contents. Documentation of inspections.

Volunteers

1-HC-2A-16
(Ref. New)

If volunteers are used in the delivery of health care, there is a documented system for selection, training, staff supervision, facility orientation, and a definition of tasks, responsibilities and authority that is approved by the health authority. Volunteers may only perform duties consistent with their credentials and training. Volunteers agree in writing to abide by all facility policies, including those relating to the security and confidentiality of information.

Comment: Facility orientation should include topics such as: fire, safety, security, and contraband.

Protocols: Written policy and procedure. Volunteer agreement forms.
Process Indicators: Signed agreement forms. Observation. Interviews with students and interns.

Students and/or Interns

1-HC-2A-17
(Ref. 3-4339)

Any students, interns, or residents delivering health care in the facility, as part of a formal training program, work under staff supervision, commensurate with their level of training. There is a written agreement between the facility and training, or educational facility that covers the scope of work, length of agreement, and any legal or liability issues. Students or interns agree in writing to abide by all facility policies, including those relating to the security and confidentiality of information.

Comment: None.

Protocols: Written policy and procedure. Written agreements or contracts.
Process Indicators: Signed agreements and contracts. Observation. Interviews.

Offender Assistants

1-HC-2A-18
(Ref. 3-4340)

Unless prohibited by state law, offenders (under staff supervision) may perform familial duties commensurate with their level of training. These duties may include the following:

- *peer support and education*
- *hospice activities*
- *assisting impaired offenders on a one-on-one basis with activities of daily living*
- *serving as a suicide companion or buddy if qualified and trained through a formal program that is part of a suicide prevention plan*

Offenders are not to be used for the following duties:

- *performing direct patient care services*
- *scheduling health care appointments*
- *determining access of other offenders to health care services*
- *handling or having access to surgical instruments, syringes, needles, medications, or health records*
- *operating diagnostic or therapeutic equipment except under direct supervision (by specially trained staff) in a vocational training program*

Comment: No offender or group of offenders is given control or authority over other offenders in the health care area.

Protocols: Written policy and procedure.
Process Indicators: Observation. Interviews.

III. Offender Treatment

PERFORMANCE STANDARD

3A. Offenders are treated humanely, fairly, and in accordance with established policy and all applicable laws.

<u>OUTCOME MEASURES</u>:

(1) Number of offender lawsuits related to unfair treatment or rights violation found in favor of the offender during the past twelve-month period divided by the number of offender lawsuits related to unfair treatment or rights violation during the past twelve-month period.

(2) Number of state court malpractice or torte liability cases found in favor of the offender during the past twelve-month period divided by the number of state court malpractice or torte liability cases during the past twelve-month period.

EXPECTED PRACTICES

Grievances

1-HC-3A-01
(Ref. New)

There is a system for resolving offender grievances relating to health care concerns.

<u>Comment</u>: None.

<u>Protocols</u>: Written policy and procedures. Grievance reporting forms.
<u>Process Indicators</u>: Grievance records. Interviews.

Notification

1-HC-3A-02
(Ref. 3-4374)

There is a process by which the individuals designated by the offender are notified in case of serious illness, serious injury, or death, unless security reasons dictate otherwise. If possible, permission for notification is obtained from the offender.

<u>Comment</u>: The persons to be notified should be designated in writing as part of the facility's admissions procedures. Whenever possible, the facility should obtain the offender's consent prior to notifying any designated individuals.

<u>Protocols</u>: Written policy and procedure.
<u>Process Indicators</u>: Notification records.

Confidentiality

1-HC-3A-03
(Ref. 3-4377)

(MANDATORY) The principle of confidentiality applies to an offender's health records and information about an offender's health status.

- *The active health record is maintained separately from the confinement case record.*
- *Access to the health record is in accordance with state and federal law.*
- *To protect and preserve the integrity of the facility, the health authority shares with the superintendent or the warden information regarding an offender's medical management.*
- *The circumstances are specified when correctional staff should be advised of an offender's health status. Only that information necessary to preserve the health and safety of an offender, other offenders, volunteers, visitors, or the correctional staff is provided.*
- *Policy determines how information is provided to correctional and classification staff, volunteers, and visitors to address the medical needs of the offender as it relates to housing, program placement, security, and transport.*

Comment: The principle of confidentiality protects offender patients from disclosure of confidences entrusted to a health care provider during the course of treatment.

Protocols: Policy and procedure.
Process Indicators: Observation. Interviews.

Informed Consent

1-HC-3A-04
(Ref. 3-4372)

(MANDATORY) Informed consent standards in the jurisdiction are observed and documented for offender care in a language understood by the offender. In the case of minors, the informed consent of a parent, guardian, or a legal custodian applies when required by law. When health care is rendered against the patient's will, it is in accordance with state and federal laws and regulations. Otherwise, any offender may refuse (in writing) medical, dental, and mental health care.

Comment: If the offender refuses to sign the refusal form, it must be signed by at least two witnesses. The form must then be sent to medical and reviewed by a qualified health care professional. If there is a concern about decision-making capacity, an evaluation should be done, especially if the refusal is for critical or acute care.

Protocols: Written policy and procedure. Consent or authorization forms.
Process Indicators: Health records. Completed consent forms. Interviews.

Elective Procedures

1-HC-3A-05
(Ref. 3-4359)

There are guidelines that govern elective procedures or surgery for offenders.

Comment: Health care staff should have a procedure for decisions on elective surgery needed to correct a substantial functional deficit or if an existing pathological process threatens the well-being of the inmate over a period of time.

Protocols: Written policy and procedure.
Process Indicators: Health records. Interviews.

Special Needs

1-HC-3A-06
(Ref. 3-4369)

There is consultation between the facility and program administrator (or a designee) and the responsible clinician (or designee) prior to taking action regarding chronically ill, physically disabled, geriatric, seriously mentally ill, or developmentally disabled offenders in the following areas:

* *housing assignments*
* *program assignments*
* *disciplinary measures*
* *transfers to other facilities*

When immediate action is required, consultation to review the appropriateness of the action occurs as soon as possible, but no later than seventy-two hours.

Comment: Maximum cooperation between custody personnel and health care providers is essential so that both groups are aware of decisions and movements regarding mentally ill and developmentally disabled offenders.

Protocols: Written policy and procedure.
Process Indicators: Documentation of consultation between facility or program administrator and clinician. Health records. Interviews.

Segregation

1-HC-3A-07
(Ref. 3-4246)

(MANDATORY) When an offender is transferred to segregation, health care personnel will be informed immediately and will provide assessment and review as indicated by the protocols established by the health authority. Unless medical attention is needed more frequently, each offender in segregation receives a daily visit from a health care provider. The visit ensures that offenders have access to the health care system. The presence of a health care provider in segregation is announced and recorded. The frequency of physician visits to segregation units is determined by the health authority.

Comment: Health care providers' visits are intended to be screening rounds and are not meant to be clinical encounters. Those offenders who request "sick call" are evaluated by a health care provider who determines the appropriate setting for further medical attention or examination. Health care providers may request that an offender be removed from a cell or housing area for medical attention or examination.

Protocols: Written policy and procedure.

Process Indicators: Health records. Segregation logs. Duty assignment roster for health care providers. Observation. Interviews.

Involuntary Administration

1-HC-3A-08
(Ref. 3-4342-1)

(MANDATORY) The involuntary administration of psychotropic medication(s) to an offender is governed by applicable laws and regulations of the jurisdiction. When administered, the following conditions must be met:

- *authorization is by a physician who specifies the duration of therapy*
- *less restrictive intervention options have been exercised without success as determined by the physician or psychiatrist*
- *details are specified about why, when, where, and how the medication is to be administered*
- *monitoring occurs for adverse reactions and side effects*
- *treatment plan goals are prepared for less restrictive treatment alternatives as soon as possible.*

Comment: None.

Protocols: Written policy and procedure. Laws and regulations.
Process Indicators: A health record. Interviews.

Research

1-HC-3A-09
(Ref. 3-4373)

(MANDATORY) The use of offenders for medical, pharmaceutical, or cosmetic experiments is prohibited. This does not preclude individual treatment of an offender based on his or her need for a specific medical procedure that is not generally available. Institutions electing to perform research will be in compliance with all state and federal guidelines.

Comment: Experimental programs include aversive conditioning, psycho-surgery, and the application of cosmetic substances being tested prior to sale to the general public. An individual's treatment with a new medical procedure by his or her physician should be undertaken only after the offender has received a full explanation of the positive and negative features of the treatment and only with informed consent.

Protocols: Written policy and procedure. Laws and regulations.
Process Indicators: Health records. Interviews.

Privacy

1-HC-3A-10
(Ref. New)

Health care encounters, including medical and mental health interviews, examinations, and procedures should be conducted in a setting that respects the offenders' privacy.

Comment: Female offenders should be provided a female escort for encounters with a male health care provider.

Protocols: Written policy and procedure. Facility diagram.
Process Indicators: Observation. Interviews.

Transfer

1-HC-3A-11
(Ref. 3-4368)

A transfer that results in an offender's placement in a noncorrectional facility or in a special unit within the facility, specifically designated for the care and treatment of the severely mentally ill or developmentally disabled, follows due process procedures as specified by federal, state, and local law prior to the move being effected. In emergency situations, a hearing is held as soon as possible after the transfer.

<u>Comment</u>: The following are generally accepted as due process procedures: written notice to the offender of the proposed transfer; a hearing for the offender, with the right (unless limited for good cause) to call and cross-examine witnesses, a decision by an independent official not involved in treatment of the offender, with a statement of the reasons for transfer; and an independent adviser to assist the offender facing transfer.

<u>Protocols</u>: Written policy and procedure. State and local law.
<u>Process Indicators</u>: Health records. Transfer logs. Interviews.

Use of Restraints

1-HC-3A-12
(Ref. 3-4362)

(MANDATORY) The use of restraints for medical and psychiatric purposes is defined, at a minimum, by the following:

- *conditions under which restraints may be applied*
- *types of restraints to be applied*
- *identification of a qualified medical or mental health professional who may authorize the use of restraints after reaching the conclusion that less intrusive measures would not be successful*
- *monitoring procedures for offenders in restraints*
- *length of time restraints are to be applied*
- *documentation of efforts for less restrictive treatment alternatives as soon as possible*
- *an after-incident review*

<u>Comment</u>: Written policy should identify the authorization needed and when, where, and how restraints may be used and for how long.

<u>Protocols</u>: Written policy and procedure. Monitoring form.
<u>Process Indicators</u>: Health records. Restraint logs. Completed monitoring forms. List of providers authorized to order restraints. Interviews.

Sexual Assault

1-HC-3A-13
(Ref. New)

Victims of sexual assault are referred under appropriate security provisions to a community facility for treatment and gathering of evidence, or if these procedures are performed in-house, the following guidelines are used:

- *A history is taken by health care professionals who conduct an examination to document the extent of physical injury and to determine if referral to another medical facility is indicated. With the victim's*

consent, the examination includes the collection of evidence from the victim, using a kit approved by the appropriate authority.
- *Provision is made for testing of sexually transmitted diseases (for example, HIV, gonorrhea, hepatitis, and other diseases) and counseling, as appropriate.*
- *Prophylactic treatment and follow-up for sexually transmitted diseases are offered to all victims, as appropriate.*
- *Following the physical examination, there is availability of an evaluation by a mental health professional to assess the need for crisis intervention counseling and long-term follow-up.*
- *A report is made to the facility or program administrator or designee to assure separation of the victim from his or her assailant.*

<u>Comment</u>: None.

<u>Protocols</u>: Written policy and procedure. Reporting form. Evidence collecting kit.
<u>Process Indicators</u>: Health records. Incident reports. Interviews.

Exercise

1-HC-3A-14
(Ref. New)

Exercise areas are available to meet exercise and physical therapy requirements of individual offender treatment plans.

<u>Comment</u>: None.

<u>Protocols</u>: Written policy and procedure. Facility diagrams and design measurements.
<u>Process Indicators</u>: Documentation of opportunity for exercise. Movement schedules and logs. Observation. Interviews.

1-HC-3A-15
(Ref. 3-4258)

Offenders in segregation are offered an opportunity to perform a minimum of one hour of exercise per day, outside their cells, five days per week, unless security or safety considerations dictate otherwise.

<u>Comment</u>: None.

<u>Protocols</u>: Written policy and procedure. Facility diagrams and design measurements.
<u>Process Indicators</u>: Documentation of opportunity for exercise. Movement schedules and logs. Observation. Interviews.

IV. Performance Improvement

PERFORMANCE STANDARD

4A. Health care services are evaluated and continually improved.

OUTCOME MEASURES:

(1) Number of problems identified by internal review that were corrected during the past twelve-month period divided by the number of problems identified by internal review during the past twelve-month period.

(2) The vacancy rate for full-time equivalents for each category within the health care staff, in other words, physicians, nursing, mid-level practitioners, ancillary staff, during the past twelve-month period.

EXPECTED PRACTICES

Quarterly Meetings

1-HC-4A-01
(Ref. 3-4328)

The health authority meets with the facility or program administrator at least quarterly and submits quarterly reports on the health services system, health environment, and submits plans to address issues raised.

Comment: Minutes of the quarterly administrative meetings may be used to meet the requirements for a quarterly report. The report should address topics such as the effectiveness of the health care system, a description of any environmental factors that need improvement, changes effected since the last reporting period, and, if needed, recommended corrective action. The health authority should report immediately any condition that poses a danger to staff or offender health and safety.

Protocols: Written policy and procedure.
Process Indicators: Documentation of meetings. Minutes and reports. Interviews.

Statistical Reports

1-HC-4A-02
(Ref. 3-4328)

Quarterly reports are prepared and include, at a minimum, the use of health care services by category, referrals to specialists, prescriptions written, laboratory and x-ray tests completed, infirmary admissions (if applicable), on-site or off-site hospital admissions, serious injuries or illnesses, deaths, and off-site transports.

Comment: Statistical reports assist in the monitoring of health care services and can be used to help justify the allocation of resources.

Protocols: Written policy and procedure. Statistical report form.
Process Indicators: Documentation of monthly statistical reports.

Internal Review and Quality Assurance

1-HC-4A-03
(Ref. New)

(MANDATORY) A system of documented internal review will be developed and implemented by the health authority. The necessary elements of the system will include:

- *participating in a multidisciplinary quality improvement committee*
- *collecting, trending, and analyzing data combined with planning, intervening, and reassessing*
- *evaluating defined data, which will result in more effective access, improved quality of care, and better utilization of resources*
- *on-site monitoring of health service outcomes on a regular basis through:*

  (a) *chart reviews by the responsible physician or his or her designee, including investigation of complaints and quality of health records*
  (b) *review of prescribing practices and administration of medication practices*
  (c) *systematic investigation of complaints and grievances*
  (d) *monitoring of corrective action plans*

- *reviewing all deaths in custody, suicides or suicide attempts, and illness outbreaks*
- *implementing measures to address and resolve important problems and concerns identified (corrective action plans)*
- *reevaluating problems or concerns to determine objectively whether the corrective measures have achieved and sustained the desired results*
- *incorporating findings of internal review activities into the organization's educational and training activities*
- *maintaining appropriate records (for example, meeting minutes) of internal review activities*
- *issuing a quarterly report to be provided to the health services administrator and facility or program administrator of the findings of internal review activities*
- *requiring a provision that records of internal review activities comply with legal requirements on confidentiality of records*

Comment: Reports can be facilitated by regular participation of the facility or program administrator, health administrator, and responsible physician. Consider having a physician as the supervisor of the program.

Protocols: Written policy and procedure. Record review format.
Process Indicators: Documentation of completed record review. Quality improvement committee minutes. Quarterly report. Interviews.

Peer Review

1-HC-4A-04
(Ref. New)

(MANDATORY) A documented external peer review program for physicians, mental health professionals, and dentists is used by the facility every two years.

Comment: The credentialing and privileging process is an integral part of assuring the competence of the providers for the inmate patients they treat. This should be routine every two years with an ability to have an immediate review if problems of practice arise. Immediate reviews are serious and only should be permitted by a careful decision of the most senior physician responsible for the system or institution. A mechanism for patient care complaints, observations by other health services providers, security, or other nonmedical providers should be established so that the responsible physician can call a panel of independent physicians to review the practice and practice patterns of the physician on whom the complaint(s) has (have) been made. The investigation and its findings are confidential in most states by statute. The responsible physician should receive the report, take indicated action, and be prepared to demonstrate to the auditors, within the confines of confidentiality, the process, process indicators, and the actions available (i.e., termination of the physician, required education in an area, prohibition against seeing a type of disease entity without another physician, etc.). It is important that the auditors appreciate that the process is real and meaningful and that peer review is not simply a paper trail without substance.

Protocols: Written policy and procedure. Written agreement or contract.
Process Indicators: Signed agreement or contract. Peer review reports.

Staffing

1-HC-4A-05
(Ref. 3-4051)

The facility uses a staffing analysis to determine the essential positions needed to perform the health services mission and provide the defined scope of services. A staffing plan is developed and implemented from this analysis. There is an annual review of the staffing plan by the health authority to determine if the number and type of staff is adequate.

Comment: Adequate staffing is based on variables such as, facility size and configuration, location, and offender type. The staffing analysis is used to determine the types and numbers of staff needed to provide a defined scope of services (medical, dental, mental health, and infirmary).

Protocols: Written policy and procedure.
Process Indicators: Documentation of annual staffing plan review. Staffing analysis plan. Interviews.

Health Records

1-HC-4A-06
(Ref. 3-4376)

The health record file (paper and/or electronic) is complete and contains the following items filed in a uniform manner:

- *patient identification on each sheet*
- *a completed receiving screening form*
- *health appraisal data forms*
- *a problem summary list*
- *a record of immunizations*
- *all findings, diagnoses, treatments, and dispositions*
- *a record of prescribed medications and their administration records, if applicable*
- *laboratory, x-ray, and diagnostic studies*
- *the place, date, and time of health encounters*
- *health service reports (for example, emergency department, dental, mental health, telemedicine, or other consultations)*
- *an individualized treatment plan, when applicable*
- *progress reports*
- *a discharge summary of hospitalization and other termination summaries*
- *a legible signature (includes electronic) and the title of the provider (may use ink, type, or stamp under the signature)*
- *consent and refusal forms*
- *release of information forms*

The method of recording entries in the records, the form and format of the records, and the procedures for their maintenance and safekeeping are approved by the health authority. The health record is made available to, and is used for documentation by all practitioners.

<u>Comment</u>: The receiving screening form should become a part of the record at the time of the first health encounter.

Protocols: Policy and procedure. Health record forms.
<u>Process Indicators</u>: Health records. Completed forms. Interviews.

Transfers

1-HC-4A-07
(Ref. 3-4378)

Nonemergency offender transfers require the following:

- *health record confidentiality to be maintained*
- *summaries, originals, or copies of the health record accompany the offender to the receiving facility; health conditions, treatments, and allergies should be included in the record*
- *determination of suitability for travel based on medical evaluation, with particular attention given to communicable disease clearance*
- *Written instructions regarding medication or health interventions required en route should be provided to transporting officers separate from the medical record*
- *specific precautions (including standard) to be taken by transportation officers (for example, masks or gloves)*

A medical summary sheet is required for all inter- and intrasystem transfers to maintain the provision of continuity of care. Information included does not require a release of information form.

<u>Comment</u>: Transfers may be permanent or temporary (for consultative or diagnostic services).

<u>Protocols</u>: Written policy and procedures. Transfer and transportation form(s).

<u>Process Indicators</u>: Health records. Completed forms. Observations. Interviews.

Inactive Records

1-HC-4A-08
(Ref. 3-4379)

Inactive health record files are retained as permanent records in compliance with the legal requirements of the jurisdiction. Health record information is transmitted to specific and designated physicians or medical facilities in the community on the written request authorization of the offender.

<u>Comment</u>: Requirements for records on juveniles may vary from those for adults.

<u>Protocols</u>: Written policy and procedures. Offender authorization forms.

<u>Process Indicators</u>: Completed facility request and offender authorization forms.

V. Offender Hygiene

PERFORMANCE STANDARD

5A. Appropriate services and supplies are provided to promote the maintenance of acceptable levels of offender hygiene.

<u>OUTCOME MEASURES</u>:

(1) Number of offenders diagnosed with hygiene-related conditions (scabies, lice, or fungal infections) during the past twelve-month period divided by the average daily population during the past twelve-month period.

(2) Number of offender grievances related to hygiene found in favor of the offender during the past twelve-month period divided by the number of offender grievances related to hygiene during the past twelve-month period.

(3) Number of offender lawsuits related to hygiene found in favor of the offender during the past twelve-month period divided by the number of offender lawsuits related to hygiene during the past twelve-month period.

EXPECTED PRACTICES

Hygiene Articles

1-HC-5A-01
(Ref. 3-4324)

Articles necessary for maintaining proper personal hygiene are available to all offenders and provided to those who are indigent. Each offender should be provided soap, toilet paper, and a toothbrush, and toothpaste, or denture cleaner and adhesives, if needed. Shaving equipment should be made available upon request, and the special hygiene needs of all offenders should be met.

<u>Comment</u>: None.

<u>Protocols</u>: Written policy and procedure.
<u>Process Indicators</u>: Documentation that items are provided. Observation. Offender interviews.

Bedding and Linen

1-HC-5A-02
(Ref. 3-4321)

There is an issue of suitable, clean bedding and linen, including two sheets, one pillow, one pillowcase, one mattress, and sufficient blankets to provide comfort under existing temperature controls. There is a provision for clean linen exchange, including towels, at least weekly.

<u>Comment</u>: Collection, storage, and exchange methods for bedding and linens should be done hygienically. Blankets, pillows, and mattresses should be

cleaned before reissue, and linens and towels must be laundered before reissue.

Protocols: Written policy and procedure. Guidelines for linen exchange.
Process Indicators: Linen exchange records. Observation. Interviews.

Clothing

1-HC-5A-03
(Ref. 3-4319)

Offenders are provided the opportunity to have three complete sets of clean clothing per week. The facility may provide this clean clothing in several ways, including access to self-service washer facilities, central clothing exchange, or a combination of the two. Wash basins in cells or rooms are not substitutes for washing facilities.

Comment: None.

Protocols: Written policy and procedure.
Process Indicators: Clothing exchange records. Observation. Interviews.

1-HC-5A-04
(Ref. New)

When standard issued clothing presents a security or medical risk (for example, suicide observation), provisions are made to supply the offender with a security garment that will promote offender safety in a way that is designed to prevent humiliation and degradation.

Comment: None.

Protocols: Written policy and procedure.
Process Indicators: Documentation of security garment use. Interviews.

Hair Care Services

1-HC-5A-05
(Ref. 3-4325)

Hair care services that comply with applicable regulatory requirements are available to offenders. Equipment should be inventoried and stored securely when not in use.

Comment: Large facilities should designate a room for hair care services small facilities may use a multipurpose room. In all cases, hair should be cut under sanitary conditions and in an area that permits observation by staff.

Protocols: Written policy and procedure. Regulatory requirements.
Process Indicators: Documentation of regulatory requirement compliance. Equipment inventory records. Observation. Interviews.

Washbasins

1-HC-5A-06
(Ref. 3-4133)

Offenders have access to operable washbasins with hot and cold running water in the medical housing unit or infirmary area at a minimum ratio of one basin for every twelve occupants, unless state or local building or health codes specify a different ratio.

Comment: None.

Protocols: Policy and procedure. Facility design diagrams.
Process Indicators: Ratio documentation. Observation.

Showers and Bathing

1-HC-5A-07
(Ref. 3-4134)

Offenders have access to operable showers with temperature-controlled hot and cold running water, at a minimum ratio of one shower for every eight offenders, unless local or state building or health codes specify a different ratio. Water for showers is thermostatically controlled to temperatures ranging from 100 degrees Fahrenheit to 120 degrees Fahrenheit to ensure the safety of offenders and to promote hygienic practices.

Comment: Offenders can use scalding showers as a weapon against, or punishment for, other offenders. Also, accidental injury could occur when cold water is drawn in other areas, thereby unexpectedly elevating the hot water in showers to scalding temperatures. Water temperatures below 100 degrees Fahrenheit are uncomfortable and may deter an individual from pursuing good hygienic practices. The temperature controls should not preclude the use of water at higher temperatures, if needed, in other areas of the facility, such as in kitchens.

Protocols: Policy and procedure. Facility design diagrams.
Process Indicators: Ratio documentation. Documentation of temperature readings. Interviews.

1-HC-5A-08
(Ref. 3-4322)

There are sufficient shower facilities in the general housing areas to permit offenders in the general population to shower at least three times per week.

Comment: Offenders in special jobs, such as those dealing with food, medical, sanitation, or mechanical services, should be encouraged to shower daily, and ideally, each offender should be permitted to shower daily.

Protocols: Policy and procedure. Facility design diagrams.
Process Indicators: Observation. Interviews.

1-HC-5A-09
(Ref. New)

There are sufficient bathing facilities in the medical housing unit and infirmary area to allow offenders housed there to bathe daily.

Comment: At least one bathing facility should be configured and equipped to accommodate offenders who have physical impairments or who need assistance to bathe.

Protocols: Policy and procedure. Facility design diagram.
Process Indicators: Number of bathing facilities. Observation. Interviews.

Toilets

1-HC-5A-10
(Ref. 3-4132)

Offenders have access to toilets and hand-washing facilities twenty-four hours per day and are able to use toilet facilities without staff assistance when they are confined in the medical housing unit or in the infirmary area. Toilets are provided at a minimum ratio of one for every twelve offenders in male facilities and one for every eight offenders in female facilities. Urinals may be substituted for up to one-half of the toilets in male facilities. All housing units with three or more offenders have a minimum of two toilets. These ratios apply unless state or local building or health codes specify a different ratio.

Comment: The standard ensures the availability of toilets and requires a measure of privacy and control for users. At the same time, the standard provides flexibility for designers and managers, who have increased options for "dry"cells if toilet facilities are accessible by other means (for example, pushbutton locks on cells for use during night hours). Creative design approaches may increase privacy and decrease management problems associated with congregate facilities.

Comment: None.

Protocols: Policy and procedure. Facility design diagrams.
Process Indicators: Documentation of ratio. Observation.

VI. Safety and Sanitation

PERFORMANCE STANDARD

6A. The facility or program is safe and sanitary.

OUTCOME MEASURES:

(1) Number of fire code violations corrected during the past twelve-month period divided by the number of fire code violations cited by jurisdictional authority during the past twelve-month period.

(2) Number of offender injuries resulting from fires requiring medical treatment in the past twelve-month period divided by the average daily population in the past twelve-month period.

(3) Number of offender injuries (other than by fire) requiring medical treatment in the past twelve-month period divided by the average daily population of offenders in the past twelve-month period.

(4) Number of staff injuries resulting from fires requiring medical treatment in the past twelve-month period divided by the average daily population of staff in the past twelve-month period.

(5) Number of staff injuries (other than fire) requiring medical treatment in the past twelve-month period divided by the average daily population of staff in the past twelve month period.

(6) Number of offender lawsuits related to safety or sanitation found in favor of the offender during the past twelve-month period divided by the number of offender lawsuits related to safety or sanitation during the past twelve-month period.

(7) Number of assaults—offender against offender, offender against staff during the past twelve-month period—divided by the average daily population in the past twelve-month period.

(8) Number of lost key incidents during the past twelve-month period.

(9) Number of health code violations corrected during the past twelve-month period divided by the number of health code violations during the past twelve-month period.

EXPECTED PRACTICES

Injury Prevention

1-HC-6A-01
(Ref. New)

There is a written plan to address offender and staff injury prevention. The plan is based on an analysis of the facility's injury experience and includes methods for identification of problems and preventive or corrective measures.

Comment: Offender injuries may be intentional or unintentional.

Protocols: Written policy and procedure. Injury or incident report form.

**1-HC-6A-02
(Ref. 3-4188)**

Process Indicators: Documentation of injury analysis. Completed injury or incident reports and investigations. Health record entries. Interviews.

(MANDATORY) Medical and dental instruments and supplies (syringes, needles, and other sharps) are controlled and inventoried.

Comment: None.

Protocols: Written policy and procedure. Inventory forms.
Process Indicators: Inventory logs and forms. Observation. Interviews.

Control of Contraband

**1-HC-6A-03
(Ref. 3-4184)**

There is a written plan accessible to staff for the control of contraband.

Comment: None.

Protocols: Written policy and procedure. Handbooks.
Process Indicators: Observation. Interviews.

Key Control

**1-HC-6A-04
(Ref. 3-4187)**

(MANDATORY) There is a written plan accessible to staff for the control of keys.

Comment: None.

Protocols: Written policy and procedure. Key control log or form.
Process Indicators: A completed key control log or forms. Observation. Interviews.

Fire Safety

**1-HC-6A-05
(Ref. 3-4121)**

(MANDATORY) The facility has an annual fire inspection by the authority having jurisdiction or other qualified person(s).

Comment: None.

Protocols: Written policy and procedure. Internal inspection forms.
Process Indicators: Copy of annual inspection.

**1-HC-6A-06
(Ref. 3-4200)**

(MANDATORY) The facility complies with the fire codes and regulations of the authority having jurisdiction.

Comment: Applicable fire codes must be followed to ensure the safety of the offenders and staff. Reports of periodic inspections and action should be maintained.

Protocols: Written policy and procedure. Copies of fire regulations. Internal inspection forms.

Process Indicators: Reports of inspections by external agencies, and licenses or certificates. Internal inspection reports. Observation. Staff interviews.

**1-HC-6A-07
(Ref. 3-4199)**

(MANDATORY) A qualified person conducts fire inspections at least quarterly or at intervals approved by the authority having jurisdiction. Equipment is tested as specified by the manufacturer or the authority having jurisdiction, whichever is more frequent.

Comment: None.

Protocols: Written policy and procedure. Internal inspection forms.
Process Indicators: Copies of completed internal inspections. Equipment testing records. Documentation of qualifications of person(s) conducting fire and/or safety inspections.

**1-HC-6A-08
(Ref. 3-4121)**

(MANDATORY) The facility has a fire alarm and automatic detection system, as approved by the authority having jurisdiction or there is a plan for addressing these or other deficiencies within a reasonable time period. The authority approves any variances, exceptions, or equivalencies that do not constitute a serious life safety threat to the occupants of the facility.

Comment: An identification system that alerts facility personnel at the earliest possible moment is critical to fire control/fire fighting and to expedite the evacuation of staff and offenders, to prevent injury and to preserve life and health.

Protocols: Written policy and procedure. Facility plan or specifications. Detection and alarm testing schedule or plan.
Process Indicators: Results of alarm/detection tests divided by the number of detection tests. Observation. Interviews.

**1-HC-6A-09
(Ref. 3-4209)**

(MANDATORY) There is a written evacuation plan to be used in the event of a fire or major emergency. The plan is certified by an independent qualified agency or individual trained in the application of national fire and safety codes. The plan is reviewed annually, updated if necessary, and reissued to the local fire jurisdiction. The plan includes the following:

- *location of building by room floor plan*
- *use of exit signs and directional arrows that are easily seen and read*
- *location of a publicly posted plan*

Comment: The evacuation plan should specify evacuation routes, and include provisions for the evacuation or transportation of incapacitated offenders and the treatment of injured staff or offenders.

Protocols: Written policy and procedure. Written emergency plan.
Process Indicators: Certification of emergency plan approval. Documentation of an annual review by the local fire jurisdiction. Documentation of credentials of person or agency that provided approval.

Flammable, Toxic, and Caustic Materials

1-HC-6A-10
(Ref. 3-4203)

(MANDATORY) All flammable, toxic, and caustic materials in the facility are controlled and secure.

Comment: Chemicals, cleaning compounds, and so forth, can cause death or serious injury. Provision should be made to ensure that offenders are never in possession of such items unless authorized and supervised by qualified personnel. Materials should be stored in appropriate storage containers in secure areas that are inaccessible to offenders and a prescribed system should be used to account for their distribution and use.

Protocols: Written policy and procedure. Inventory forms.
Process Indicators: Documentation of perpetual inventory. Observation. Interviews.

1-HC-6A-11
(Ref. 3-4202)

(MANDATORY) Noncombustible containers are used for combustible refuse. Special containers are provided for refuse containing flammable materials. All containers are emptied daily.

Comment: None.

Protocols: Written policy and procedure. Container placement diagram.
Process Indicators: Observation. Interviews.

Facility Sanitation

1-HC-6A-12
(Ref. 3-4310)

(MANDATORY) The facility complies with all applicable health codes and regulations of the governing jurisdiction, and there is documentation by an independent, outside source that any past deficiencies noted in annual inspections have been corrected. Copies of all inspections will be forwarded to both the facility or program administrator and the health authority. The following facility inspections are required:

- *weekly sanitation inspections of all facility areas by a qualified departmental staff member*
- *comprehensive and thorough monthly inspections by a safety or sanitation specialist*
- *at least annual inspections by federal, state, and/or local sanitation and health officials or other qualified person(s)*

Comment: The safety or sanitation specialist responsible for conducting monthly inspections may be a facility staff member who is trained in the application of jurisdictional codes and regulations. Periodically and on an as-needed basis, this individual is provided assistance from specialists regarding safety and sanitation requirements and inspections. Training for this individual may be provided through the agency's central office specialist(s) or by other applicable agencies.

Protocols: Written policy and procedure. Inspection codes or regulations.
Process Indicators: Documentation of weekly, monthly, or annual inspections. Documentation of qualifications of the inspector. Interviews.

Food Service Employees

1-HC-6A-13
(Ref. 3-4303)

(MANDATORY) Food service employees comply with all sanitation and health codes enacted by state or local authorities for food service employees. All persons involved in the preparation of food receive a pre-assignment health examination and periodic reexaminations to ensure freedom from diarrhea, skin infections, and other illnesses transmissible by food or utensils. Offenders and other persons working in food service are monitored each day for health and cleanliness by the director of food services (or this person's designee). All food handlers are instructed to wash their hands upon reporting to duty and after using toilet facilities. When the facility's food services are provided by an outside agency or individual, the facility has written verification that the outside provider complies with the state and local regulations regarding food services.

Comment: All employee health and sanitation codes are to be strictly followed to ensure the health and welfare of offenders and staff.

Protocols: Written policy and procedure. State or local sanitation and health codes or regulations.
Process Indicators: Documentation of health exams and daily monitoring of food service workers. Observation. Interviews.

Food Service Inspections

1-HC-6A-14
(Ref. 3-4305)

(Mandatory) Weekly inspections of all food service areas, including dining and food preparation areas and equipment, are conducted by medical, dietary, or other qualified personnel. Refrigerator and water temperatures are checked daily.

Comment: All areas and equipment related to food preparation (for example, ranges, ovens, refrigerators, mixers, dishwashers, and garbage disposals) require frequent inspections to ensure their sanitary and operating condition. Water temperature on the final dishwasher rinse should be 180 degrees Fahrenheit; between 140 degrees Fahrenheit and 160 degrees Fahrenheit is appropriate if a sanitizer is used on the final rinse.

Protocols: Written policy and procedure.
Process Indicators: Inspection reports. Temperature logs. Observation. Interviews.

Vermin and Pests

1-HC-6A-15
(Ref. 3-4313)

Vermin and pests are controlled within the facility.

Comment: None.

Protocols: Written policy and procedure.
Process Indicators: Inspection forms or logs. Observation. Interviews.

VII. Administration

PERFORMANCE STANDARD

7A. The program is administered efficiently and responsibly.

<u>OUTCOME MEASURES</u>: None.

EXPECTED PRACTICES

General Administration

1-HC-7A-01
(Ref. 3-4003)

The program has established measurable goals and objectives that are reviewed at least annually and updated, as needed.

<u>Comment</u>: None.

<u>Protocols</u>: Written policy and procedure. Written long-range goals and policies. Format for periodic review and reporting. Bylaws and constitution. Budget and planning documents. Administrative manual.
<u>Process Indicators</u>: An annual report. Board meeting minutes. Documentation of an annual review. Monthly and quarterly reports.

1-HC-7A-02
(Ref. New)

There is an internal system for assessing the achievement of goals and objectives and that documents findings. Program changes are implemented, as necessary, in response to findings.

<u>Comment</u>: Operations and programs should be implemented as outlined in the policies and procedures. An audit system providing timely and periodic assessment of the various agency operations will reveal the degree of compliance. The internal administrative audit should exist apart from any external or continuing audit conducted by other agencies.

<u>Protocols</u>: Written policy and procedure. Internal monitoring system and forms. Inspection forms. Copies of statutes.
<u>Process Indicators</u>: Inspection or internal audit reports. Documentation of corrective actions taken.

1-HC-7A-03
(Ref. 3-4329)

Each policy, procedure, and program in the health care delivery system is reviewed at least annually by the appropriate health care authority and revised, if necessary. Each document bears the date of the most recent review or revision and the signature of the reviewer.

<u>Comment</u>: None.

<u>Protocols</u>: Written policy and procedure.
<u>Process Indicators</u>: Documentation of annual review.

Organization

1-HC-7A-04
(Ref. 3-4011)

There is a written document that describes the program's organization. The description includes an organizational chart that groups similar functions, services, and activities in administrative subunits. The chart is reviewed at least annually and updated, if needed.

Comment: A current organizational chart is necessary to provide a clear administrative picture. The chart should reflect the span of control, lines of authority, and an orderly channel of communication.

Protocols: Written policy and procedure. Organizational chart or table of organization. Job descriptions. Bylaws. Articles of incorporation. Personnel manual.
Process Indicators: Personnel records. Documentation of an annual review.

Offender's Death

1-HC-7A-05
(Ref. 3-4375)

Authorities having jurisdiction are promptly notified of an offender's death. Procedures specify and govern the actions to be taken in the event of the death of an offender.

Comment: The medical examiner or coroner should be notified of the offender's death immediately. A postmortem examination should be performed if the cause of death is unknown, if the death occurred under suspicious circumstances, or if the offender was not under current medical care.

Protocols: Written policy and procedure.
Process Indicators: Documentation of actions taken.

Communication

1-HC-7A-06
(Ref. 3-4016)

There are regular meetings, at least monthly, between the administrator and key staff members.

Comment: Regular channels of communication are necessary for delegating authority, assigning responsibility, supervising work, and coordinating efforts.

Protocols: Written policy and procedure.
Process Indicators: Monthly meeting minutes.

1-HC-7A-07
(Ref. 3-4017)

There is a system of communication among all levels of staff and offenders.

Comment: None.

Protocols: Written policy and procedure.
Process Indicators: Documentation of communication. Offender records.

Physical Plant

1-HC-7A-08
(Ref. New)

Adequate space is provided for administrative, direct care, professional, and clerical staff. This space includes conference areas, a storage room for records, and toilet facilities.

Comment: None.

Protocols: Written policy and procedure. Program plans and specifications.
Process Indicators: Observation.

1-HC-7A-09
(Ref. 3-4333)

Equipment, supplies and materials for health services are provided and maintained as determined by the health authority.

Comment: The type of equipment will depend on the level of health care provided in the institution. Equipment should be checked and tested periodically and secured from inmate access.

Protocols: Written policy and procedure.
Process Indicators: An equipment checklist. Inventory records.

PERFORMANCE STANDARD

7B. Staff is treated fairly.

OUTCOME MEASURES:

(1) Number of grievances filed by staff in the past twelve months divided by the number of full-time equivalent staff positions in the past twelve months.

(2) Number of staff grievances decided in favor of staff in the past twelve months divided by the total number of staff grievances in the past twelve months.

(3) Total number of years of staff members' experience in the field as of the end of the last calendar year divided by the number of staff at the end of the last calendar year (for example, the average number of years of experience).

(4) Number of staff termination or demotion hearings in which the program decision was upheld in the past twelve months divided by the number of staff termination or demotion hearings requested in the past twelve months.

EXPECTED PRACTICES

Personnel Policies

1-HC-7B-01
(Ref. 3-4048)

A personnel manual is accessible to employees that covers, at a minimum, the following areas:

- *an organizational chart*
- *staff development*
- *recruitment and selection*
- *promotion*
- *job qualifications and job descriptions*

- *affirmative action*
- *sexual harassment*
- *grievance and appeal procedures*
- *orientation*
- *employee evaluation*
- *personnel records*
- *benefits*
- *holidays*
- *leave*
- *hours of work*
- *probationary period*
- *compensation*
- *travel*
- *disciplinary procedures*
- *termination*
- *resignation*
- *an employee assistance program*
- *code of ethics*
- *conflict of interest*
- *legal assistance*

Employees are required to sign statements acknowledging access to and awareness of personnel policies and regulations.

Comment: The program's personnel policy should reflect its management philosophy and cover all areas relevant to the welfare of the personnel.

Protocols: Written policy and procedure. Personnel manual. Distribution and dissemination plans for this manual.
Process Indicators: Documentation of distribution. Signed receipts from each employee.

1-HC-7B-02
(Ref. 3-4053)   ***Equal employment opportunities exist for all positions.***

Comment: None.

Protocols: Written policy and procedure.
Process Indicators: Interviews.

1-HC-7B-03
(Ref. 3-4054)   ***The program does not discriminate against nor exclude qualified ex-offenders from employment.***

Comment: Ex-offenders can be a valuable resource and should not be discriminated against when they seek employment with the agency. Qualified applicants should have the opportunity to prove that they can be productive employees.

Protocols: Written policy and procedure. Hiring policies.
Process Indicators: Personnel records.

1-HC-7B-04
(Ref. 3-4063)

Compensation and benefit levels for all personnel are comparable to similar occupational groups in the state or region.

Comment: Competitive salaries and benefits are necessary for the recruitment and retention of high-caliber staff.

Protocols: Written policy and procedure. Wage and compensation scale. Documentation of the local jurisdiction's wage scale. Salary schedules.
Process Indicators: Payroll records.

1-HC-7B-05
(Ref. 3-4065)

The facility maintains a current, accurate, confidential personnel record on each employee. Information obtained as part of a required medical examination (and/or inquiry) regarding the medical condition or history of applicants and employees is collected and maintained on separate forms and in separate medical files, and treated as a confidential medical record.

Comment: The personnel record should contain the following items: the initial application; reference letters; the results of the employment investigation; verification of training and experience; wage and salary information; job performance evaluations; incident reports, if any; and commendations and disciplinary actions, if any.

Protocols: Written policy and procedure. Applicable statutes. Personnel forms.
Process Indicators: Personnel records.

1-HC-7B-06
(Ref. 3-4066)

Employees may challenge information in their personnel file. The information will be corrected or removed, if proved inaccurate.

Comment: Employees should be allowed to review their personnel files to ensure that they are current and accurate. Written procedure should specify the means for correcting discrepancies.

Protocols: Written policy and procedure.
Process Indicators: Personnel records.

1-HC-7B-07
(Ref. 3-4062)

Employees receive an annual written performance review. The review is based on defined criteria, and the results are discussed with the employee.

Comment: Performance reviews should be an ongoing process with written evaluations, completed at least annually. Reviews should be objective and based on specific job criteria and explicit performance standards.

Protocols: Written policy and procedure.
Process Indicators: Personnel records. Interviews.

PERFORMANCE STANDARD

7C. The program is a responsible member of the community.

OUTCOME MEASURES: None.

EXPECTED PRACTICES

Volunteer Services

1-HC-7C-01
(Ref. 3-4113)

The program provides for recruiting citizens for involvement and for volunteers. The screening and selection of volunteers allow for recruitment from all cultural and socioeconomic parts of the community.

Comment: Volunteers can make an important contribution to an agency by providing a number of direct services to offenders, and by serving as a link between the agency and the community. The written policies and procedures should explain the major functions and method of operation of volunteer services. Staff responsibility for maintaining citizen involvement in the agency should be clearly designated. Efforts should be made to recruit volunteers from all segments of society. Volunteers should be selected based on a uniform screening process that is consistent with security concerns.

Protocols: Written policy and procedure. A volunteer recruiting plan.
Process Indicators: Documentation of volunteer recruiting activities.

1-HC-7C-02
(Ref. 3-4116)

Each volunteer completes an appropriate, documented orientation and/or training program prior to assignment.

Comment: None.

Protocols: Written policy and procedure. A volunteer handbook. A training curriculum. Training forms.
Process Indicators: Volunteer records. Training documentation.

1-HC-7C-03
(Ref. 3-4114)

There is an official registration and identification system for volunteers.

Comment: All volunteers should be registered with the program or parent agency for insurance purposes, and each volunteer should be issued an identification card. The program should maintain an identification record for each volunteer that includes a photograph, an address, current telephone number, and other relevant information.

Protocols: Written policy and procedure. Volunteer orientation and registration procedures. An identification system.
Process Indicators: Volunteer records.

Appendix A

Health Care Outcome Measure Worksheet

		Health Care Outcomes		
Standard	Outcome Measure	Numerator/Denominator	Value	Outcome Measure
1A	(1)	Number of offenders with a positive tuberculin skin test in the past 12 months		
	divided by	Annual number of admissions in the past 12 months		
	(2)	Number of offenders diagnosed with active tuberculosis in the past 12 months		
	divided by	Average daily population in the past 12 months		
	(3)	Number of conversions to a positive tuberculin skin tests given in the past 12 months		
	divided by	Number of tuberculin skin tests given in the past 12 months		
	(4)	Number of offenders with a positive tuberculin skin test who completed prophylaxis treatment for tuberculosis in the past 12 months		
	divided by	Number of offenders with a positive tuberculin skin test on prophylaxis treatment for tuberculosis in the past 12 months		
	(5)	Number of Hepatitis C positive offenders in the past 12 months		
	divided by	Average daily population in the past 12 months		
	(6)	Number of HIV-positive offenders in the past 12 months		
	divided by	Average daily population in the past 12 months		
	(7)	Number of HIV-positive offenders who are being treated with highly active antiretroviral treatment in the past 12 months		
	divided by	Number of known HIV-positive offenders in the past 12 months		
	(8)	Number of offenders diagnosed with an Axis I diagnosis (excluding sole diagnosis of substance abuse) in the past 12 months		
	divided by	Average daily population in the past 12 months		
	(9)	Number of offender suicide attempts in the past 12 months		
	divided by	Average daily population in the past 12 months		

(continued)

Health Care Outcome Measure Worksheet (cont.)

Standard	Outcome Measure	Numerator/Denominator	Value	Outcome Measure
	(10)	Number of offender suicides in the past 12 months		
	divided by	Average daily population in the past 12 months		
	(11)	Number of deaths due to homicide in the past 12 months		
	divided by	Average daily population in the past 12 months		
	(12)	Number of deaths due to injuries in the past 12 months		
	divided by	Average daily population in the past 12 months		
	(13)	Number of medically expected deaths in the past 12 months		
	divided by	Average daily population in the past 12 months		
	(14)	Number of medically unexpected deaths in the past 12 months		
	divided by	Average daily population in the past 12 months		
	(15)	Number of offender admissions to infirmary (where available) in the past 12 months		
	divided by	Average daily population in the past 12 months		
	(16)	Number of offender admissions to off-site hospitals in the past 12 months		
	divided by	Average daily population in the past 12 months		
	(17)	Number of offenders transported off-site (via ambulance or correctional vehicle) for treatment of emergency health conditions in the past 12 months		
	divided by	Average daily population in the past 12 months		
	(18)	Number of offender speciality consults completed in the past 12 months		
	divided by	Number of specialty consults (onsite or off-site) ordered by primary health care provider (MD, NP, PA) in the past 12 months		
	(19)	Number of offender grievances about access to healthcare services found in favor of the offender in the past 12 months		
	divided by	Number of offender grievances about access to healthcare services in the past 12 months		
	(20)	Number of offender grievances related to quality of health care found in favor of offender during the past 12 month period		
	divided by	Number of offender grievances related to quality of health care during the past 12 month period		

(continued)

Health Care Outcome Measure Worksheet (cont.)

Standard	Outcome Measure	Numerator/Denominator	Value	Outcome Measure
	(21)	Number of offender grievances related to unfair treatment or rights violation found in favor of the offender during a 12 month period		
	divided by	Number of offender grievances related to unfair treatment or rights violation during a 12 month period.		
	(22)	Number of offender grievances related to safety or sanitation found in favor of the offender during a 12 month period		
	divided by	Number of offender grievances related to safety or sanitation during a 12 month period		
	(23)	Number of offender lawsuits about access to healthcare services found in favor of the offender during the past 12 month period.		
	divided by	Number of offender lawsuits about access to healthcare services during the past 12 months		
	(24)	Number of individual sick call encounters during the past 12 month period		
	divided by	Average daily population in the past 12 months		
	(25)	Number of physician visit during the past 12 month period		
	divided by	Average daily population in the past 12 months		
	(26)	Number of individualized dental treatment plans during the past 12 month period.		
	divided by	Average daily population in the past 12 months		
	(27)	Number of hypertensive offenders enrolled in chronic care clinic in the past 12 months		
	divided by	Average daily population in the past 12 months		
	(28)	Number of diabetic offenders enrolled in chronic care clinic in the past 12 months		
	divided by	Average daily population in the past 12 months		
	(29)	Number of incidents involving pharmaceuticals as contraband in the past 12 months		
	divided by	Average daily population in the past 12 months		
	(30)	Number of cardiac diets received by offenders with cardiac disease in the past 12 months		
	divided by	Number of cardiac diets prescribed in the past 12 months		
	(31)	Number of hypertensive diets received by offenders with hypertension in the past 12 months		
	divided by	Number of hypertensive diets prescribed during the past 12 month period		

(continued)

Health Care Outcome Measure Worksheet (cont.)

Standard	Outcome Measure	Numerator/Denominator	Value	Outcome Measure
	(32)	Number of diabetic diets received by offenders with diabetes in the past 12 months		
	divided by	Number of diabetic diets prescribed in the past 12 months		
	(33)	Number of renal diets received by offenders with renal disease in the past 12 months		
	divided by	Number of renal diets prescribed in the past 12 months		
	(34)	Number of needle stick injuries in the past 12 months		
	divided by	Number of employees on average in the past 12 months		
	(35)	Number of pharmacy-dispensing errors in the past 12 months		
	divided by	Number of prescriptions dispensed by the pharmacy in the past 12 months		
	(36)	Number of nursing-medication-administration errors in the past 12 months		
	divided by	Number of medications administered in the past 12 months		
2A	**(1)**	Number of staff with lapsed licensure and or certification during the past 12 month period		
	divided by	Number of licensed and or certified staff during the past 12 month period		
	(2)	Number of new employees during the past 12 month period who completed orientation training prior to undertaking job assignments.		
	divided by	Number of new employees during the past 12 month period		
	(3)	Number of employees completing in-service training requirements in the past 12 months		
	divided by	Number of employees eligible in the past 12 months		
	(4)	Number of staff turnover per position category (MD, RN, LPN, medical records, and so forth) during the past 12 month period		
	divided by	Number of staff positions per category in the past 12 months		
	(5)	Number of staff terminations for violation of drug-free work policy during the past 12 month period		
	divided by	Number of staff terminations during the past 12 month period		

(continued)

Health Care Outcome Measure Worksheet (cont.)

Standard	Outcome Measure	Numerator/Denominator	Value	Outcome Measure
3A	(1)	Number of offender lawsuits related to unfair treatment or rights violation found in favor of the offender during the past 12 month period.		
	divided by	Number of offender lawsuits related to unfair treatment or rights violation during the past 12 month period		
	(2)	Number of state court malpractice or torte liability cases found in favor of the offender during the past 12 month period		
	divided by	Number of state court malpractice or torte liability cases during the past 12 month period		
4A	(1)	Number of problems identified by internal review that were corrected during the past 12 month period		
	divided by	Number of problems identified by internal review during during the past 12 month period		
	(2)	Vacancy rate for full-time equivalents for each category within the health care staff, in other words, physician, nursing, midlevel practitioner, ancillary staff, during the past 12 month period		
5A	(1)	Number of offenders diagnosed with hygiene related conditions (scabies, lice, fungal infections) during the past 12 month period		
	divided by	Average daily population during the past 12 month period		
	(2)	Number of offender grievances related to hygiene found in favor of the offender during the past 12 month period		
	divided by	Number of offender grievances related to hygiene during the past 12 month period		
	(3)	Number of offender lawsuits related to hygiene found in favor of the offender during the past 12 month period		
	divided by	Number of offender lawsuits related to hygiene during the past 12 month period		
6A	(1)	Number of fire code violations corrected during the past 12 month period		
	divided by	Number of fire code violations cited by jurisdictional authority during the past 12 month period		
	(2)	Number of offender injuries resulting from fires requiring medical treatment during the past 12 month period.		
	divided by	Average daily population during the past 12 month period		

(continued)

Health Care Outcome Measure Worksheet (cont.)

Standard	Outcome Measure	Numerator/Denominator	Value	Outcome Measure
	(3)	Number of offender injuries (other than fire) requiring medical treatment in the past 12 month period		
	divided by	Average daily population of offenders in the past 12 month period.		
	(4)	Number of staff injuries resulting from fires requiring medical treatment in the past 12 month period		
	divided by	Average daily population of staff in the past 12 month period.		
	(5)	Number of staff injuries (other than fire) requiring medical treatment in the past 12 month period		
	divided by	Average daily population of staff in the past 12 month period.		
	(6)	Number of offender lawsuits related to safety or sanitation found in favor of the offender during the past 12 month period		
	divided by	Number of offender lawsuits related to safety or sanitation during the past 12 month period		
	(7)	Number of assaults: offender/offender, offender/staff during the past 12 month period		
	divided by	Average daily population in the past 12 month period.		
	(8)	Number of lost key incidents during the past 12 month period		
	(9)	Number of health code violations corrected during the past 12 month period		
	divided by	Number of health code violations during the past 12 month period		
7A	None			
7B	(1)	Number of grievances filed by staff in the past twelve months		
	divided by	Number of full-time equivalent staff positions in the past twelve months		
	(2)	Number of staff grievances decided in favor of staff in the past twelve months		
	divided by	Total number of staff grievances in the past twelve months		
	(3)	Total number of years of staff members' experience in the field as of the end of the last calendar year		

(continued)

Health Care Outcome Measure Worksheet (cont.)

Standard	Outcome Measure	Numerator/Denominator	Value	Outcome Measure
	divided by	Number of staff at the end of the last calendar year (for example, average number of years of experience)		
	(4)	Number of staff termination or demotion hearings in which the program decision was upheld in the past twelve months		
	divided by	Number of staff termination or demotion hearings requested in the past twelve months		
7C	None			

Appendix B

Partial Sample of Health Care Outcome Measure Worksheet

	Sample of Health Care Outcomes			
Standard	Outcome Measure	Numerator/Denominator	Value	Outcome Measure
1A	**(1)**	Number of offenders with a positive tuberculin skin test in the past 12 months	10	
	divided by	Annual number of admissions in the past 12 months	100	0.1
	(2)	Number of offenders diagnosed with active tuberculosis in the past 12 months	25	
	divided by	Average daily population in the past 12 months	500	0.05
	(3)	Number of conversions to a positive tuberculin skin test in the past 12 months	2	
	divided by	Number of tuberculin skin tests given in the past 12 months	100	0.02
	(4)	Number of offenders with a positive tuberculin skin test who completed prophylaxis treatment for tuberculosis on an annual basis	25	
	divided by	Number of offenders with a positive tuberculin skin test on prophylaxis treatment for tuberculosis in the past 12 months	25	0
	(5)	Number of Hepatitis C positive offenders in the past 12 months	75	
	divided by	Average daily population in the past 12 months	500	0.15
	(6)	Number of HIV-positive offenders in the past 12 months	34	
	divided by	Average daily population in the past 12 months	500	0.068
	(7)	Number of HIV-positive offenders who are being treated with highly active antiretroviral treatment in the past 12 months	53	
	divided by	Number of known HIV-positive offenders in the past 12 months	125	0.424
	(8)	Number of offenders diagnosed with an Axis I diagnosis (excluding sole diagnosis of substance abuse) in the past 12 months	183	
	divided by	Average daily population in the past 12 months	500	0.366

Appendix C

Guidelines for the Control and Use of Flammable, Toxic, and Caustic Substances

This appendix provides definitions and recommendations to assist agencies in the application of standards that address the control of materials that present a hazard to staff and inmates.

Substances that do not contain any of the properties discussed in the guidelines but are labeled "Keep out of reach of children" or "May be harmful if swallowed" are not necessarily subject to the controls specified in the guidelines. Their use and control, however, including the quantities available, should be evaluated and addressed in agency policy. Questions concerning the use and control of any substance should be resolved by examining the manufacturer's Material Safety Data Sheet.

I. DEFINITIONS

Flash point—the minimum temperature at which a liquid will give off sufficient vapors to form an ignitable mixture with the air near the surface of the liquid (or in the vessel used).

Flammable liquid—A substance with a flash point below 100 Fahrenheit (37.8 degrees Centigrade). Classified by flash point as a Class I liquid. (*See* Table A.)

Combustible liquid—A substance with a flash point at or above 100 Fahrenheit. Classified by flash point as a Class II or Class III liquid. (*See* Table A.)

Toxic material—A substance that, through chemical reaction or mixture, can produce possible injury or harm to the body by entry through the skin, digestive tract, or respiratory tract. The toxicity is dependent on the quantity absorbed and the rate, method, and site of absorption. (*See* Table A.)

Caustic material—A substance capable of destroying or eating away by chemical reaction. (*See* Table A.)

It is possible that a substance may possess more than one of the above properties; therefore, the safety requirements for all applicable properties should be considered.

II. GENERAL GUIDELINES

A. Issuance
All flammable, caustic, and toxic substances should be issued (e.g., drawn from supply points to canisters or dispensed) only under the supervision of authorized staff.

B. Amounts
All such substances should be issued only in the amount necessary for one day's needs.

C. Supervision
All persons using such substances should be closely supervised by qualified staff.

D. Accountability
All such substances must be accounted for before, during, and after their use.

TABLE A
Common Flammable, Toxic, and Caustic Substances

Class I Liquids
Gasoline
Benzine (Petroleum ether)
Acetone
Hexane
Lacquer
Lacquer thinner
Denatured alcohol
Ethyl alcohol
Xylene (Xylol)
Contact cement (flammable)
Toludi (Toluene)
Methyl ethyl ether
Methyl ethyl ketone
Naphtha Y, M, and P

Class II Liquids
Diesel fuel
Motor oil
Kerosene
Cleaning solvents
Mineral spirits
Agitene

Class III Liquids
Paints (oil base)
Linseed oil
Mineral oil
Neatsfoot oil
Sunray conditioner
Guardian fluid

Toxic Substances
Ammonia
Chlorine
Antifreeze
Duplicating fluid
Methyl alcohol (Wood alcohol or Methanol)
Defoliants
Herbicides
Pesticides
Rodenticides

Caustic Substances
Lye
Muriatic acid
Caustic soda
Sulfuric acid
Tannic acid

III. SPECIFIC GUIDELINES FOR STORAGE, USE, AND DISPOSAL

A. Flammable and Combustible Liquids
Any liquid or aerosol that is required to be labeled "flammable" or "combustible" under the Federal Hazardous Substances Labeling Act must be stored and used according to label recommendations and in a way that does not endanger life and property.

1. Storage
Lighting fixtures and electrical equipment in flammable liquid storage rooms must conform to the National Electrical Code requirements for installation in hazardous locations.

Storage rooms must meet the following specifications:

- be of fire-resistant construction and properly secured
- have self-closing fire doors at all openings
- have either a four-inch sill or a four-inch depressed floor (inside storage rooms only)
- have a ventilation system either mechanical or gravity flow within twelve inches of the floor that provides at least six air changes per hour in the room

Each storage cabinet must be:

- properly constructed and securely locked
- conspicuously labeled "Flammable Keep Fire Away"
- used to store no more than sixty gallons of Class I or Class II liquids or 120 gallons of Class III liquids.

Storage rooms and cabinets must be properly secured and supervised by an authorized staff member any time they are in use. Doors and cabinets shall be placed so that they do not obstruct access to exits, stairways, and other areas normally used for evacuation in the event of fire or other emergency.

All portable containers for flammable and combustible liquids other than the original shipping containers must be in approved safety cans listed or labeled by a nationally recognized testing laboratory. Containers should bear legible labels identifying the contents.

All excess liquids should remain in their original container in the storage room or cabinet. All containers should be tightly closed when not in use.

2. Use

The use of any flammable or combustible liquid must conform with the provisions and precautions listed in the manufacturer's Material Safety Data Sheet.

Flammable and combustible liquids can be dispensed only by an authorized staff member. The only acceptable methods for drawing from or transferring these liquids into containers inside a building are (1) through a closed piping system, (2) from safety cans, (3) by a device drawing through the tip, or (4) by gravity through an approved self-closing system. An approved grounding and bonding system must be used when liquids are dispensed from drums.

Only liquids with a flash point at or above 100 degrees Fahrenheit (e.g., Stoddard solvents, kerosene) can be used for cleaning. Such operations must be performed in an approved parts cleaner or dip-tank fitted with a fusible link lid with a 160 degree Fahrenheit melting-temperature link. *Under no circumstances may flammable liquids be used in cleaning.*

3. Disposal

Excess flammable or combustible liquids must be disposed of properly. The Material Safety Data Sheet for each substance prescribes the proper method of disposal and related precautions.

4. Spills

Information on the proper course of action for chemical spills is contained in the Material Safety Data Sheet for each substance.

B. Toxic and Caustic Substances

1. Storage

All toxic and caustic materials are to be stored in their original containers in a secure area in each department. The manufacturer's label must be kept intact on the container.

2. Use

Toxic and caustic substances can be drawn only by a staff member. The Material Safety Data Sheet for each substance details the necessary provisions and precautions for its use.

Unused portions are to be returned to the original container in the storage area or, if appropriate, stored in the storage area in a suitable, clearly labeled container.

3. Disposal

See disposal guidelines for Flammable and Combustible Liquids above.

4. Spills

See spills guidelines for Flammable and Combustible Liquids above.

C. Poisonous Substances

Poisonous substances or chemicals are those that pose a very high (Class I) caustic hazard due to their toxicity. Examples: Methyl alcohol, sulfuric acid, muriatic acid, caustic soda, tannic acid. There are special precautions on the control and use of methyl alcohol (also known as wood alcohol or methanol), which is a flammable, poisonous liquid commonly used in industrial applications (e.g., shellac, thinner, paint solvent, duplicating fluid, solvents for leather, cements, and dyes, flushing fluid for hydraulic brake systems). *Drinking methyl alcohol can cause death or permanent blindness.*

The use of any product containing methyl alcohol must be directly supervised by staff. Products containing methyl alcohol in a diluted state, such as shoe dye, may be issued to inmates or residents, but only in the smallest workable quantities.

Immediate medical attention is imperative whenever methyl alcohol poisoning is suspected.

D. Other Toxic Substances

1. Permanent antifreeze containing ethylene glycol should be stored in a locked area and dispensed only by authorized staff.

2. Typewriter cleaner containing carbon tetrachloride or tricholorochane should be dispensed in small quantities and used under direct supervision.

3. The use of cleaning fluid containing carbon tetrachloride or tetrachloride or tricholoroethylene must be strictly controlled.

4. Glues of all types may contain hazardous chemicals and should receive close attention at every stage of handling. Nontoxic products should be used when possible. Toxic glues must be stored under lock and used under close supervision.

5. The use of dyes and cements for leather requires close supervision. Nonflammable types should be used whenever possible.

6. Ethyl alcohol, isopropyl alcohol, and other antiseptic products should be stored and used only in the medical department. The use of chemicals must be closely supervised. Whenever possible, such chemicals should be diluted and issued only in small quantities so as to prevent any injurious or lethal accumulation.

7. Pesticides contain many types of poisons. The staff member with responsibility for the facility's safety program should be responsible for purchasing, storing, and dispensing any pesticide. All pesticides should be stored under lock. NOTE: Only chemicals approved by the Environmental Protection Agency shall be used. DDT and 1080 (sodium fluoracetate) are among those chemicals absolutely prohibited.

8. Herbicides must be stored under lock. The staff member responsible for herbicides must have a current state license as a Certified Private Applicator. Proper clothing and protective gear must be used when applying herbicides.

9. Lyes must be used only in dye solutions and only under the direct supervision of staff.

IV. RESPONSIBILITIES

A. Inventories

Constant inventories should be maintained for all flammable, toxic, and caustic substances used and stored in each department. A bin record card should be maintained for each such substance to accurately reflect acquisitions, disbursements, and the amounts on hand.

B. Departmental Files

Each department using any flammable, toxic, or caustic substance should maintain a file of the manufacturer's Material Safety Data Sheet for each substance. This file should be updated at least annually. The file also should contain a list of all areas where these substances are stored, along with a plant diagram and legend. A copy of all information in the file, including the Material Safety Data Sheets, should be supplied to the staff member responsible for the facility's safety program.

C. Master Index

The person responsible for the facility's safety program should compile a master index of all flammable, caustic, and toxic substances in the facility, including their locations and Material Safety Data Sheets. This information should be kept in the safety office (or comparable location) and should be supplied to the local fire department. The master index should also contain an up-to-date list of emergency phone numbers (e.g., local fire department, local poison control center).

D. Personal Responsibility

It is the responsibility of each person using these substances to follow all prescribed safety precautions, wear personal protective equipment when necessary, and report all hazards or spills to the proper authority. The protection of life, property, and our environment depends on it.

Appendix D

Definition of "Qualified Individual" for Safety and Sanitation Inspections

Several expected practices refer to documentation and inspections by "qualified individuals." (For example, Environmental Conditions [1A], Vehicles [1B], Fires [1C], and Food Service [4C], expected practices.) Such persons also may be referred to as "independent, qualified source," "qualified departmental staff member," "qualified designee," or "qualified fire and safety officer."

A "qualified individual" is a person whose training, education, and/or experience specifically qualifies him or her to do the job indicated in the standard.

I. General Requirements

When an expected practice calls for inspections, the individual conducting them needs to be trained in the application of appropriate codes and regulations. Expected practices do not specify the number of hours of training required, as this is determined in part by the tasks assigned. At a minimum, though, the qualified individual must (1) be familiar with the applicable codes and regulations and their requirements; (2) be able to use the appropriate instruments for measuring and documenting code compliance; (3) be able to complete checklists and prepare the necessary reports; and (4) have the authority to make corrections when deficiencies are found.

Training is often obtained from code officials or inspectors (fire marshals, building officials); government agencies that have statutory authority for inspections in a particular area (health department, labor department); or private organizations, such as the National Fire Protection Association. Often the individual obtains written certification or approval from these authorities to conduct in-house inspections. When trained and certified by the above sources to do so, a central office specialist may train and assist facility staff to conduct inspections.

II. SPECIFIC REQUIREMENTS

A. Authority Having Jurisdiction

The term " authority having jurisdiction" is defined as follows:

> The authority having jurisdiction must be knowledgeable about the requirements of the National Fire Protection Life Safety Code. The authority having jurisdiction must be a federal, state, local, or other regional department or individual, such as the fire chief, fire marshal, chief of a fire prevention bureau, labor department, health department, building official, electrical inspector, or others with statutory authority. The authority having jurisdiction may be employed by the department/agency, provided that he or she is not under the authority of the facility administrator and that the report generated is referred to higher authorities within the department/agency independent of influence by the facility administrator or staff. This rule applies no matter who generates the report.

The definition also applies to the terms "independent, qualified source" and "independent, outside source."

B. Inspections

Qualified individuals conducting the monthly and weekly inspections required in the standards may be institutional staff members.

The qualified individual responsible for conducting monthly inspections (e.g., fire and safety officer, safety/sanitation specialist) may be an institutional staff member trained in the application of jurisdictional codes and regulations. Periodically and as needed, this individual receives assistance from the independent authority or central office specialist(s) on requirements and inspections. This assistance may include participation in quarterly or bi-annual inspections. Training for the individual conducting the monthly inspections may be provided by the applicable agencies or through the agency's central office specialist(s).

The qualified departmental staff member who conducts weekly inspections of the facility may be an institutional staff member who has received training in and is familiar with the safety and sanitation requirements of the jurisdiction. At a minimum, on-the-job training from the facility's safety/sanitation specialist or the fire and safety officer regarding applicable regulations is expected, including use of checklists and methods of documentation.

The periodic weekly and monthly inspections may be conducted by either a combination of qualified individuals or one specialist, as long as the schedules and minimum qualifications described above are met. Safety and sanitation inspections may be conducted by the same person, provided this individual is familiar with the regulations for both types of inspections. When safety and sanitation requirements differ substantially, it may sometimes be necessary to call on several qualified individuals to conduct the inspections required by the expected practices. Using more than one person is strongly recommended.

III. COMPLIANCE AUDITS

In conducting compliance audits, Commission Visiting Committees will review documentation submitted by the facilities to assist them in judging the qualifications of these individuals. In making compliance decisions, the audit teams will look closely at the facility's entire program, both practices and results, for ensuring safety and sanitation.

Glossary

Absconder—A juvenile who fails to report for probation or aftercare supervision or an escapee or runaway from a juvenile placement.

Adjudicatory hearing—A hearing to determine whether the allegations of a petition are supported by the evidence beyond a reasonable doubt or by the preponderance of the evidence.

Administrative segregation—A form of separation from the general population administered by the classification committee or other authorized group when the continued presence of the inmate in the general population would pose a serious threat to life, property, self, staff, or other inmates or to the security or orderly running of the institution. Inmates pending investigation for trial on a criminal act or pending transfer also can be included. (*See Protective custody* and *Segregation.*)

Administrator—See Program director.

Administrator of field services—The individual directly responsible for directing and controlling the operations of the adult probation and/or parole field services program. This person may be a division head in a large correctional agency, a chief probation officer answering to a judge, or the administrative officer of a court or parole authority with responsibility for the field services program.

Admission—The process of entry into a program. During admission processing, the juvenile or adult offender receives an orientation to program goals, rules, and regulations. Assignment to living quarters and to appropriate staff also is completed at this time.

Adult community residential service—Also referred to as halfway house, a community-based program providing group residence (such as a house, work release center, prerelease center) for probationers, parolees, residents in incarcerated status, and referrals through the courts or other agencies. Clients also may receive these services from the agency on a nonresidential basis. (See Out-client.)

Adult correctional institution—A confinement facility, usually under state or federal auspices, that has custodial authority over adults sentenced to confinement for more than one year.

Adult detention facility or Jail—A local confinement facility with temporary custodial authority. Adults can be confined pending adjudication for forty-eight hours or more and usually for sentences of up to two years.

Affirmative action—A concept designed to ensure equal opportunity for all persons regardless of race, religion, age, sex, or ethnic origin. These equal opportunities include all personnel programming, such as selection, promotion, retention, rate of pay, demotion, transfer, layoff, and termination.

Aftercare—Control, supervision, and care exercised over juveniles released from facilities through a stated release program. (*See Releasing authority.*)

Agency—The unit of a governing authority that has direct responsibility for the operations of a corrections program, including the implementation of policy as set by the governing authority. For a community residential center, this would be the administrative headquarters of the facilities. A single community facility that is not a part of a formal consolidation of community facilities is considered to be an agency. In a public agency, this could be a probation department, welfare department, or similar agency. For a juvenile correctional organization, this would be the central office responsible for governing the juvenile correctional system for the jurisdiction.

Agency administrator—The administrative officer appointed by the governing authority or designee who is responsible for all operations of the agency, such as the department of corrections or parole, and all related programs under his or her control.

Agency industries administrator—The individual who has functional responsibility for industries operations throughout the correctional system. Titles, such as head of industries, superintendent, chief, director, or general manager, may be used to denote this position.

Alternative meal service—Special foods provided to comply with the medical, religious or security requirements. Alternative meals always must be designed to ensure that basic health needs are met and are provided in strict compliance with the policies signed by the chief executive officer, the chief medical officer, and for the religious diets, by the appropriate religious leader.

Audit—An examination of agency or facility records or accounts to check their accuracy. It is conducted by a person or persons not directly involved in the creation and maintenance of these records or accounts. An independent audit results in an opinion that either affirms or disaffirms the accuracy of records or accounts. An operational or internal audit usually results in a report to management that is not shared with those outside the agency.

Booking—Both a law enforcement process and a detention-facility procedure. As a police administrative action, it is an official recording of an arrest and the identification of the person, place, time, arresting authority, and reason for the arrest. In a detention facility, it is a procedure for the admission of a person charged with or convicted of an offense, which includes searching, fingerprinting, photographing, medical screening, and collecting personal history data. Booking also includes the inventory and storage of the individual's personal property.

Boot camp—A short-term correctional unit designed to combine elements of basic military training programs and appropriate correctional components.

Camp—A nonsecure residential program located in a relatively remote area. The residents participate in a structured program that emphasizes outdoor work, including conservation and related activities. There are often twenty to sixty residents in these facilities.

Career development plan—The planned sequence of promotions within an agency that contains provision for (1) vertical movement throughout the entire range of a particular discipline, (2) horizontal movement encouraging lateral and promotional movement among disciplines, and (3) opportunity for all to compete for the position of head of the agency. Progression along these three dimensions can occur as long as the candidate has the ambition, ability, and required qualifications.

Case conference—A conference between individuals working with the juvenile or adult offender to see that court-ordered services are being provided.

Casework—The function of the caseworker, social worker, or other professional in providing social services, such as counseling, to individuals in custody.

Cellblock—A group or cluster of single and/or multiple occupancy cells or detention rooms immediately adjacent and directly accessible to a day or activity room. In some facilities, the cellblock consists of a row of cells fronted by a day-room of corridor-like proportions.

Chemical agent—An active substance, such as tear gas, used to defer activities that might cause personal injury or property damage.

Chemical dependency—A compulsive use of alcohol or other drugs to the point that stopping is difficult and causes physical and mental reactions.

Chief—See *Agency industries administrator.*

Chief of police—A local law enforcement official who is the appointed or elected chief executive of a police department and is responsible for the operation of the city jail or lockup.

Chronic care—Health care provided to patients over a long period of time; health care services provided to patients with long-term health conditions or illnesses. Care usually includes initial assessment, treatment, and periodic monitoring to evaluate the patient's condition.

Chronic illness—a disease process or condition that persists over an extended period of time. Chronic illnesses include diabetes, hypertension, asthma, HIV, seizures, and mental health diagnosis.

Clinical services—health care services administered to offenders in a clinic setting by persons qualified to practice in one of the health care disciplines.

Clinicians—persons qualified to assess, evaluate and treat patients according to the dictates of their professional practice act. These may include physicians, nurses, physician assistants, nurse practitioners, dentists, psychologists, psychiatrists, and social workers.

Classification—A process for determining the needs and requirements of those for whom confinement has been ordered and for assigning them to housing units and programs according to their needs and existing resources.

Co-correctional facility—An institution designed to house both male and female juvenile or adult offenders.

Code of ethics—A set of rules describing acceptable standards of conduct for all employees.

Committing authority—The agency or court responsible for placing a juvenile in a program.

Communicable disease—A disease that can be transmitted from person to person.

Community based program—See Adult community residential service.

Community resources—Human services agencies, service clubs, citizen interest groups, self-help groups, and individual citizen volunteers that offer services, facilities, or other functions that can meet the needs of the facility or have the potential to assist residents. These various resources, which may be public or private and national or local, may assist with material and financial support, guidance, counseling, and supportive services.

Continuity of care—Health care provided on a continual basis beginning with the offender's initial contact with health care personnel and all subsequent health care encounters including referrals to community providers/facilities for offsite care during incarceration and when discharged from the institution.

Contraband—Any item possessed by confined juvenile or adult offenders or found within the facility that is illegal by law or expressly prohibited by those legally charged with the administration and operation of the facility or program.

Contractor—A person or organization that agrees to furnish materials or to perform services for the facility or jurisdiction at a specified price. Contractors operating in correctional facilities are subject to all applicable rules and regulations of the facility.

Contractual arrangement—An agreement with a private party (such as an incorporated agency or married couple) to provide services to juvenile or adult offenders for compensation. (*See Independent operator.*)

Control center—A very secure, self-contained unit designed to maintain the security of the facility. Policies governing the design, staffing and accessibility of the control center ensure that it cannot be commandeered by unauthorized persons.

Controlled substance—Any drug regulated by the Drug Enforcement Act.

Copayment—A fee charged an offender by the correctional institution for health care or other services.

Corporal punishment—Any act of inflicting punishment directly on the body, causing pain or injury.

Correctional facility—A facility used for the incarceration of individuals accused of or convicted of criminal activity. A correctional facility is managed by a single chief executive officer with broad authority for the operation of the facility. This authorization typically includes the final authority for decisions concerning (1) the employment or termination of staff members, and (2) the facility operation and programming within guidelines established by the parent agency or governing body.

A correctional facility also must have (1) a separate perimeter that precludes the regular commingling of the inmates with inmates from other facilities, (2) a separate facility budget managed by a chief executive officer within guidelines established by the parent agency or governing authority, and (3) staff that are permanently assigned to the facility.

Counseling—Planned use of interpersonal relationships to promote social adjustment. Counseling programs provide opportunities to express feelings verbally with the goal of resolving the individual's problems. At least three types of counseling may be provided: individual (a one-to-one relationship), small-group counseling, and large-group counseling in a living unit.

County parole—The status of a county jail inmate who, convicted of a misdemeanor and conditionally released from a confinement facility prior to the expiration of his or her sentence, has been placed under supervision in the community for a period of time.

Credentials—Documentation that demonstrates health care professionals are qualified and currently licensed, certified, and/or registered as applicable to provide health services within their scope of practice.

Criminal-type offender—See *Delinquent youth.*

Delinquent act—An act that, if committed by an adult, would be considered a crime.

Delinquent youth—Also referred to as a juvenile delinquent or a criminal-type offender, a juvenile who has been charged with or adjudicated for conduct that would, under the law of the jurisdiction in which the offense was committed, be a crime if committed by an adult. (*See also Status offender* and *Juvenile.*)

Dental exam—An examination by a licensed dentist that includes a dental history, exploration and charting of teeth, examination of the oral cavity, and x-rays.

Dental screen—A visual assessment of the teeth and gums by a dentist or health care staff trained by a dentist. Documentation of findings includes referrals made for dental treatment.

Detainee—Any person confined in a local detention facility not serving a sentence for a criminal offense.

Detainer—A warrant placed against a person in a federal, state, or local correctional facility that notifies the holding authority of the intention of another jurisdiction to take custody of that individual when he or she is released.

Detention warrant—A warrant that authorizes the arrest and temporary detention of a parolee pending preliminary revocation proceedings. A detention warrant should be distinguished from a warrant for the return of a parolee to prison, although return warrants are sometimes used as detainers. For the purpose of these standards, return warrants used as detainers also are deemed to be detention warrants.

Detoxification—The treatment of a person who is demonstrating symptoms of intoxication or withdrawal and/or the process of gradually withdrawing alcohol or drugs from a person who is chemically dependent.

Developmental disabilities—A disorder in which there is a delay in the expected age specific development stages. These disabilities originate prior to age twenty-one, can be expected to continue indefinitely, and may constitute a substantial impairment in behavior and coping skills.

Direct supervision—A method of inmate management that ensures continuing direct contact between inmates and staff by posting an officer(s) inside each housing unit. Officers in general housing units are not separated from inmates by a physical barrier. Officers provide frequent, nonscheduled observation of and personal interaction with inmates.

Director—See *Agency industries administrator.*

Disability—A physical or mental impairment that substantially limits one or more of the major life activities of an individual; a record of such an impairment; or being regarded as having such an impairment.

Disciplinary detention—A form of separation from the general population in which inmates committing serious violations of conduct regulations are confined by the disciplinary committee or other authorized group for short periods of time to individual cells separated from the general population. Placement in detention only may occur after a finding of a rule violation at an impartial hearing and when there is not an adequate alternative disposition to regulate the inmate's behavior. (*See Protective custody* and *Segregation.*)

Disciplinary hearing—A nonjudicial administrative procedure to determine if substantial evidence exists to find an inmate guilty of a rule violation.

Dispositional hearing—A hearing held subsequent to the adjudicatory hearing to determine what order of disposition (for example, probation, training school, or foster home) should be made concerning a juvenile adjudicated as delinquent.

Diversion—The official halting or suspension, at any legally prescribed point after a recorded justice system entry, of formal criminal or juvenile justice proceedings against an alleged offender. The suspension of proceedings may be in conjunction with a referral of that person to a treatment or care program administered by a nonjudicial agency or a private agency, or there may be no referral.

Due process safeguards—Those procedures that ensure just, equal, and lawful treatment of an individual involved in all stages of the juvenile or criminal justice system, such as a notice of allegations, impartial and objective fact finding, the right to counsel, a written record of proceedings, a statement of any disposition ordered with the reasons for it, and the right to confront accusers, call witnesses, and present evidence.

Ectoparasites—Parasites that live on the outside of the host. Examples: fleas, lice.

Education program—A program of formal academic education or a vocational training activity designed to improve employment capability.

Educational release—The designated time when residents or inmates leave the program or institution to attend school in the community and return to custody after school hours.

Emergency—Any significant disruption of normal facility or agency procedure, policy, or activity caused by riot, escape, fire, natural disaster, employee action, or other serious incident.

Emergency care—Care of an acute illness or unexpected health care need that cannot be deferred until the next scheduled sick call. Emergency care shall be provided to the resident population by the medical director, physician, or other staff, local ambulance services, and/or outside hospital emergency rooms. This care shall be expedited by following specific written procedures for medical emergencies described in the standards.

Environmental health—All conditions, circumstances, and surrounding influences that affect the health of individuals or groups in the area.

Facility—A place, institution, building (or part thereof), set of buildings, or area (whether or not enclosing a building or set of buildings) that is used for the lawful custody and/or treatment of individuals. It may be owned and/or operated by public or private agencies and includes the staff and services as well as the buildings and grounds.

Facility administrator—Any official, regardless of local title (for example sheriff, chief of police, administrator, warden/superintendent) who has the ultimate responsibility for managing and operating the facility.

Field agency—The unit of a governing authority that has direct responsibility for the provision of field supervision services and for the carrying out of policy as set by the governing authority.

Field services—Services provided to delinquent juveniles, status offenders, or adult offenders in the community by probation, parole, or other agencies.

Field staff/field workers—The professionals assigned case responsibility for control, supervision, and provision of program services to delinquent juveniles or adult offenders.

First aid—Care for a condition that requires immediate assistance from an individual trained in first aid care and the use of the facility's first aid kits.

Fiscal position control—The process that ensures that individuals on the payroll are legally employed, positions are authorized in the budget, and funds are available.

Footcandle—A unit for measuring the intensity of illumination, defined as the amount of light thrown on a surface one foot away from the light source.

Formulary—A list of prescription and nonprescription medications that have been approved by the health authority and are stocked or routinely procured for use in an institution.

Furlough/Temporary leave—A period of time during which a resident is allowed to leave the facility and go into the community unsupervised.

Good-time—A system established by law whereby a convicted offender is credited a set amount of time, which is subtracted from his or her sentence, for specified periods of time served in an acceptable manner.

Governing authority—In public/governmental agencies, the administrative department or division to which the agency reports; the policy-setting body. In private agencies, this may be an administrative headquarters, central unit, or the board of directors or trustees.

Grievance/Grievance process—A circumstance or action considered to be unjust and grounds for complaint or resentment and/or a response to that circumstance in the form of a written complaint filed with the appropriate body.

Halfway house—See *Adult community residential service.*

Handicapped—Having a mental or physical impediment or disadvantage that substantially limits an individual's ability to use programs or services.

Head of industries—See *Agency industries administrator.*

Health agency—An organization that provides health care services to an institution or a system of institutions.

Health appraisal—The physician, health administrator, or agency-designated individual responsible for the coordination and management of health services within an institution.

Health authority—The health administrator, or agency responsible for the provision of health care services at an institution or system of institutions; the responsible physician may be the health authority.

Health care—The sum of all action taken, preventative and therapeutic, to provide for the physical and mental well-being of a population. It includes medical and dental services, mental health services, nursing, personal hygiene, dietary services, and environmental conditions.

Health care personnel—Individuals whose primary duty is to provide health services to inmates in keeping with their respective levels of health care training or experience.

Health care provider—An individual licensed in the delivery of health care.

Health care services—A system of preventative and therapeutic services that provide for the physical and mental well-being of a population. Includes medical and dental services, mental health services, nursing, pharmaceutical servcies, personal hygiene, dietary services, and environmental conditions.

Health/medical screen—A structured inquiry and observation to prevent newly arrived offenders who pose a health or safety threat to themselves or others from being admitted to the general population and to identify offenders who require immediate medical attention. The screen can be initiated at the time of admission by health care personnel or by a health trained correctional officer.

Health-trained personnel/Medically trained personnel—Correctional officers or other correctional personnel who may be trained and appropriately supervised to carry out specific duties with regard to the administration of health care.

Hearing—A proceeding to determine a course of action, such as the placement of a juvenile or adult offender, or to determine guilt or innocence in a disciplinary matter. Argument, witnesses, or evidence are heard by a judicial officer or administrative body in making the determination.

Hearing examiner—An individual appointed by the parole authority who conducts hearings for the authority. His or her power of decision making may include, but not be limited to, making parole recommendations to granting, denying, or revoking parole.

Holding facility/Lockup—A temporary confinement facility, for which the custodial authority is usually less than forty-eight hours, where arrested persons are held pending release, adjudication, or transfer to another facility.

Holidays—All days legally designated as nonworkdays by statute or by the chief governing authority of a jurisdiction.

House parent—See *Program director*.

Improvement—See *Quality assurance*.

Independent operator—A person or persons who contract with a correctional agency or other governmental agency to operate and manage a correctional program or facility.

Independent source—A person, organization or group that acts independently from the correctional unit being evaluated. An independent source may not be a staff member who reports to the chief executive officer of the unit being audited.

Indigent—An individual with no funds or source of income.

Industries—An activity existing in a correctional system that uses inmate labor to produce goods and/or services for sale. These goods and/or services are sold at prices calculated to recover all or a substantial portion of costs associated with their production and may include a margin of profit. Sale of the products and/or services is not limited to the institution where the industries activity is located.

Infection control program—A program designed to investigate, prevent, and control the spread of infections and communicable disease.

Infirmary—A specific area within aninstitution, separate from other housing areas, where offenders are admitted for health observation and care under the supervision and direction of health care personnel.

Information system/Management information system—The concepts, personnel, and supporting technology for the collection, organization, and delivery of information for administrative use. There are two such types of information: (1) standard information, consisting of the data required for operations control such as the daily count, payroll data in a personnel office, probation/parole success rates, referral sources, and caseload levels; (2) demand information, consisting of information that can be generated when a report is required, such as information on the number of residents in educational and training programs, duration of residence, or the number of residents eligible for discharge during a twelve-month period by offense, sentence, and month of release.

Informed consent—The agreement by a patient to a treatment, examination, or procedure after the patient receives the material facts regarding the nature, consequences, risks, and alternatives concerning the proposed treatment, examination, or procedure.

Inmate—Any individual, whether in pretrial, unsentenced, or sentenced status, who is confined in a correctional facility.

Institution industries manager—The individual designated as responsible for industries operations at a specific institution in the correctional system.

Interstate compact for the supervision of probationers and parolees—An agreement entered into by eligible jurisdictions in the United States and its territories that provides the criteria for these jurisdictions to cooperate in working with probation and release.

Interstate compact on juveniles—An agreement authorizing the interstate supervision of juvenile delinquents. This can also include the cooperative institutionalization of special types of delinquent juveniles, such as psychotics and defective delinquents.

Jail—See *Adult detention facility.*

Judicial review—A proceeding to reexamine the course of action or continued confinement of a juvenile in a secure detention facility. Arguments, witnesses, or evidence are not required as part of the review. Reviews may be conducted by a judge, judicial officer, or an administrator who has been delegated the authority to release juveniles from secure detention with the approval of the judge.

Juvenile—A person under the age of twenty-one, or as defined in the local jurisdiction as under the age of majority.

Juvenile community residential program—A program housed in a structure without security fences and security hardware or other major restraining construction typically associated with correctional facilities, such as a converted apartment building or private home. They are not constructed as or intended to be detention facilities. Except for daycare programs, they provide twenty-four-hour care, programs, and supervision to juveniles in residence. Their focus is on providing the juvenile with positive adult models and program activities that assist in resolving problems specific to this age group in an environment conducive to positive behavior in the community.

Juvenile correction center—See *Training school.*

Juvenile day treatment program—A program that provides services to juveniles who live at home and report to the program on a daily basis. Juveniles in these programs require more attention than that provided by probation and aftercare services. Often the program operates its own education program through the local school district. The population usually is drawn from court commitments but may include juveniles enrolled as a preventive or diversionary measure. The program may operate as part of a residential program, and it may provide space for occasional overnight stays by program participants where circumstances warrant additional assistance.

Juvenile delinquent—See *Delinquent youth.*

Juvenile detention—Temporary care of juvenile offenders and juveniles alleged to be delinquent who require secure custody in a physically restricting facility.

Juvenile development center—See *Training school.*

Juvenile group home—A nonsecure residential program emphasizing family-style living in a home-like atmosphere. Program goals are similar to those for large community residential programs. Although group homes usually house juveniles who are court-committed, they also house abused or neglected juveniles who are placed by social agencies. Small group homes serve from four to eight juveniles; large group homes serve eight-to-twelve. Participating juveniles range in age from ten to seventeen, with the concentration from thirteen to sixteen.

Juvenile intake—The process of determining whether the interests of the public or the juvenile require the filing of a petition with the juvenile court. Generally, an intake officer receives, reviews, and processes complaints, recommends detention or release, and provides services for juveniles and their families, including diversion and referral to other community agencies.

Juvenile ranch—A nonsecure residential program providing services to juveniles in a rural setting. Typically, the residents participate in a structured program of education, recreation, and facility maintenance, including responsibility for the physical plant, its equipment, and livestock. Often there are twenty-to-sixty juveniles in the ranch setting, ranging in age from thirteen-to-eighteen.

Juvenile service center—See *Training school.*

Juvenile village—See *Training school.*

Life Safety Code—A manual published and updated by the National Fire Protection Association specifying minimum standards for fire safety necessary in the public interest. Two chapters are devoted to correctional facilities.

Lockup—See *Adult detention facility*; *Holding facility.*

Major equipment—All equipment that is securely and permanently fastened to the building or any equipment with a current book value of $1,000 or more.

Major infraction—A rule violation involving a grievous loss and requiring imposition of due process procedures. Major infractions include (1) violations that may result in disciplinary detention or administrative segregation; (2) violations for which punishment may tend to increase an inmate's sentence; (3) violations that may result in a forfeiture, such as loss of good-time or work time; and (4) violations that may be referred for criminal prosecution.

Management information system—See *Information system.*

Medical records—Separate records of medical examinations and diagnoses maintained by the responsible physician. The date and time of all medical examinations and copies of standing or direct medical orders from the physician to the facility staff should be transferred to the resident's record.

Medical restraints—Either chemical restraints, such as sedatives, or physical restraints, such as straitjackets, applied only for medical or psychiatric purposes. Metal handcuffing and leg shackles are not considered medical restraints.

Medical screening—A system of structured observation, the initial health assessment to identify newly arrived juvenile or adult offenders who pose a health or safety threat to themselves or others.

Medically trained personnel—See *Health-trained personnel.*

Medication administration—The process of giving a dose of a prescribed or over-the-counter medication to a patient.

Medication dispensing—The process of placing one or more doeses of a medication into a container that is labeled to indicate the name of the patient, the contents of the container, and other necessary information by an individual licensed to perform such an activity.

Medication disposal—The destruction or removal of medication from a facility after discontinuation of its use.

Mental health staff—Individuals whose primary duty is to provide mental health services to inmates in keeping with their respetive levels of education, experience, training, and credentials.

Mental illness—Psychiatric illness or disease expressed primarily through abnormalities of thought, feeling, and behavior producing either distress and/or impaired function.

Mentally retarded—Describes an individual who functions at a subaverage general intellectual level and is deficient in adaptive behavior.

Midlevel practitioner—A nurse practitioner or physician assistant licensed or credentialed to assume an expanded role in providing medical care under the supervision of a physician.

NFPA—the National Fire Protection Association, which publishes the Life Safety Code.

National uniform parole reports system—A cooperative effort sponsored by the National Parole Institute that calls for the voluntary cooperation of all federal and state authorities having responsibility for felony offenders in developing some common terms to describe parolees—their age, sex, and prior record—and some common definitions to describe parole performance. These types of data allow comparisons across states and other jurisdictions.

Nonformulary medication—Medications not listed in the institution or agency formulary.

Not applicable—A term used in the accreditation process to describe a standard that does not apply to the correctional unit being audited. While the initial determination of applicability is made by ACA staff and/or the audit team, the final decision rests with the hearing panel.

Offender—An individual convicted or adjudicated of a criminal offense.

Official personnel file—A current and accurate record of the employee's job history, including all pertinent information relating to that history.

Operating unit—One distinct operation of the industry's activity, which may be operated as a cost center or separate accounting entity. It may take the form of a manufacturing operation (for example, furniture making or clothing production), an agricultural operation (for example, dairy or poultry farming, crop or orchard farming, cow or pig farming), or a service activity (for example, a warehouse, keypunch operation, microfilming process, laundering, auto repair, and so forth).

Out-client—An individual who does not live at the facility but who may use facility services and programs.

Outcome measure—Measurable events, occurrences, conditions, behaviors, or attitudes that demonstrate the extent to which a condition described has been achieved.

Occupational exposure—The exposure to potentially harmful chemical, physical, or biological agents that occur as a result of one's occupation.

Parent—The individual with whom a juvenile regularly lives and who is the natural, adoptive, or surrogate parent.

Parent government organization/Parent agency—The administrative department or division to whom the agency seeking accreditation reports; the policy-setting body.

Parole authority/Parole board/Parole commission—The decision-making body that has responsibility to grant, deny, and/or revoke parole. The term "parole authority" includes all of these bodies.

Parole hearing—A procedure conducted by a parole authority member and/or hearing examiner in which all pertinent aspects of an eligible inmate's case are reviewed to make a decision or recommendation that would change the inmate's legal status and/or degree of freedom.

Peer review—The process of having patient care provided by a clinician reviewed and evaluated by a peer with similar credentials. An external peer review is completed by a medical professional not employed by the facility being reviewed.

Permanent status—A personnel status that provides due process protection prior to dismissal.

Petition—An application for a court order or other judicial action. For example, a delinquency petition is an application for the court to act in the matter of a juvenile apprehended for a delinquent act.

Physical examination—A thorough evaluation of a patient's current physical condition and medical history conducted by or under the supervision of a licensed professional.

Placing authority—The agency or body with the authority to order a juvenile into a specific dispositional placement. This may be the juvenile court, the probation department, or another duly constituted and authorized placement agency.

Plan of action—A description of action steps designed to correct a condition that has caused a determination of noncompliance with a standard.

Policy—A course or line of action adopted and pursued by an agency that guides and determines present and future decisions and actions. Policies indicate the general course or direction of an organization within which the activities of the personnel must operate. They are statements of guiding principles that should be followed in directing activities toward the attainment of objectives. Their attainment may lead to compliance with standards and compliance with the overall goals of the agency or system.

Population center—A geographical area containing at least 10,000 people, along with public safety services, professional services, employment and educational opportunities, and cultural/recreational opportunities.

Preliminary hearing—A hearing at which it is determined whether probable cause exists to support an allegation of parole violation, pending a revocation hearing by the parole authority.

Pretrial release—A procedure whereby an accused individual who had been taken into custody is allowed to be released before and during his or her trial.

Probation—A court-ordered disposition alternative through which a convicted adult offender or an adjudicated delinquent is placed under the control, supervision, and care of a probation field staff member.

Procedure—The detailed and sequential actions that must be executed to ensure that a policy is fully implemented. It is the method of performing an operation or a manner of proceeding on a course of action. It differs from a policy in that it directs action in a particular situation to perform a specific task within the guidelines of policy.

Process indicators—Documentation and other evidence that can be examined periodically and continuously to determine that practices are being implemented properly.

Professional association—A collective body of individuals engaged in a particular profession or vocation. The American Correctional Association, the American Medical Association, and the National Association of Clinical Psychologists are examples of professional associations, of which there are hundreds in the United States.

Professional staff—Social workers, probation officers, and other staff assigned to juvenile and adult offender cases. These individuals generally possess bachelor's degrees and advanced training in the social or behavioral sciences.

Program—The plan or system through which a correctional agency works to meet its goals; often this program requires a distinct physical setting, such as a correctional institution, community residential facility, group home, or foster home.

Program director/Administrator/Superintendent/Houseparent—The individual directly in charge of the program.

Protective custody—A form of separation from the general population for inmates requesting or requiring protection from other inmates for reasons of health or safety. The inmate's status is reviewed periodically by the classification committee or other designated group. (*See Administrative segregation* and *Disciplinary detention.*)

Prosthesis—A functional or cosmetic, artificial device that substitutes for a missing body part such as an arm, leg, eye, or tooth.

Protocols—Written instructions that guide implementation of expected practices, such as policies and procedures, training curriculum, offender handbooks, diagrams, and internal forms and logs.

Psychotropic medication—A drug that exerts an effect on thought, mood, and behavior. Psychotropic medications are used to treat various disorders as well as mental illness.

Qualified medical person—An individual who has the education, credentials, and experience, and is permitted by law within the scope of his or her professional practice act, to evaluate and care for patients.

Qualified mental health person—An individual who has the education, credentials, and experience, and is permitted by law withing the scope of his or her professional practice act, to evaluate and care for the mental health needs of patients.

Quality assurance/Improvement—A formal, internal monitoring program that uses standardized criteria to endure quality and consistency. The program identifies opportunities for improvement, develops improvement strategies, and monitors their effectiveness.

Records (juvenile and adult offenders)—Information concerning the individual's delinquent or criminal, personal, and medical history and behavior and activities while in custody, including but not limited to commitment papers, court orders, detainers, personal property receipts, visitors' lists, photographs, fingerprints, type of custody, disciplinary infractions and actions taken, grievance reports, work assignments, program participation, and miscellaneous correspondence.

Referral—The process by which a juvenile or adult offender is introduced to an agency or service that can provide the assistance needed.

Release on bail—The release by a judicial officer of an accused individual who has been taken into custody on the accused's promise to appear in court as required for criminal proceedings.

Releasing authority—The decision-making body and/or individual who has the responsibility to grant, deny, and revoke release from a juvenile institution or program of supervision. In some jurisdictions, it is called the parole board or the parole commission. (*See Aftercare.*)

Renovation—A significant structural or design change in the physical plant of a facility.

Responsible physician—An individual licensed to practice medicine and provide health services to the inmate population of the facility and/or the physician at an institution with final responsibility for decisions related to medical judgments.

Revocation hearing—A hearing before the parole authority at which it is determined whether revocation of parole should be made final.

Safety equipment—Primarily firefighting equipment, such as chemical extinguishers, hoses, nozzles, water supplies, alarm systems, sprinkler systems, portable breathing devices, gas masks, fans, first aid kits, stretchers, and emergency alarms.

Safety vestibule—In a correctional facility, a grill cage that divides the inmate areas from the remainder of the institution. They must have two doors or gates, only one of which opens at a time, to permit entry to or exit from inmate areas in a safe and controlled manner.

Sally port—An enclosure situated in the perimeter wall or fence of a correctional facility containing gates or doors at both ends, only one of which opens at a time, ensuring there will be no breach in the perimeter security of the institution. The sally port may handle either pedestrian or vehicular traffic.

School or home for boys and girls—*See Training center.*

Secure institution—Any facility that is designed and operated to ensure that all entrances and exits are under the exclusive control of the facility's staff, thereby not allowing an inmate/resident to leave the facility unsupervised or without permission.

Security or Custody—The degree of restriction of inmate movement within a detention/correctional facility, usually divided into maximum, medium, and minimum risk levels.

Security devices—Locks, gates, doors, bars, fences, screens, ceilings, floors, walls, and barriers used to confine and control detained individuals. Also included are electronic monitoring equipment, security alarm systems, security lights, auxiliary power supplies, and other equipment used to maintain facility security.

Security perimeter—The outer portions of a facility that provide for secure confinement of facility inmates/residents. The design of the perimeter may vary depending on the security classification of the facility.

Segregation—The confinement of an inmate to an individual cell that is separated from the general population. There are three forms of segregation: administrative segregation, disciplinary detention, and protective custody.

Self-insurance coverage—A statewide system designed to insure the payment of all legal claims for injury or damage incurred as a result of the actions of state officials, employees, or agents. In public agencies, the self-insurance program is usually authorized by the legislature. A "memorandum of insurance" or similar document is required that acts as a policy, setting the limits of liability for various categories of risk, including deductible limits. Approval of the policy by a cabinet-level official is also required.

Serious incident—A situation in which injury serious enough to warrant medical attention occurs involving a resident, employee, or visitor on the grounds of the institution. Also, a situation containing an imminent threat to the security of the institution and/or to the safety of residents, employees, or visitors on the grounds of the institution.

Severe mental disturbance—A condition in which an individual is a danger to self or others or is incapable of attending to basic physiological needs.

Shelter facility—Any nonsecure public or private facility designated to provide either temporary placement for alleged or adjudicated status offenders prior to the issuance of a disposition order or longer-term care under a juvenile court disposition order.

Sheriff—The elected or appointed chief executive officer of a county law enforcement agency. Sheriffs can serve several functions, including responsibility for law enforcement in unincorporated areas, operation of the county jail, and assignment as officers of the court.

Special management inmates—Individuals whose behavior presents a serious threat to the safety and security of the facility, staff, general inmate population, or themselves. Special handling and/or housing is required to regulate their behavior.

Special needs—A mental and/or physical condition that requires different accommodations or arrangements than a general population offender normally would receive. Offenders with special needs may include, but are not limited to, the emotionally disturbed, developmentally disabled, mentally ill, physically handicapped, chronically ill, the disabled or infirm, and the drug or alcohol addicted.

Standard—A statement that defines a required or essential condition to be achieved or maintained.

Status offender—A juvenile who has been charged with or adjudicated for conduct that under the law of the jurisdiction in which the offense was committed that would not be a crime if committed by an adult. *(See also Delinquent youth.)*

Strip search—An examination of an inmate's/resident's naked body for weapons, contraband, and physical abnormalities. This also includes a thorough search of all of the individual's clothing while it is not being worn.

Superintendent—See *Agency industries administrator; Program director; Warden.*

Temporary leave—See Furlough.

Temporary release—A period of time during which an inmate is allowed to leave the program or institution and go into the community unsupervised for various purposes consistent with the public interest.

Therapeutic diet—A diet prescribed by a health care practitioner as part of the patient's medical treatment. Therapeutic diets can be ordered by physicians, physician's assistants, or nurse practitioners.

Training—An organized, planned, and evaluated activity designed to achieve specific learning objectives and enhance the job performance of personnel. Training may occur on site, at an academy or training center, an institution of higher learning, during professional meetings, or through contract service or closely supervised on-the-job training. It includes a formal agenda and instruction by a teacher, manager, or official; physical training; or other instruction programs that include a trainer/trainee relationship. Training programs usually include requirements for completion, attendance recording, and a system for recognition of completion. Meetings of professional associations are considered training where there is clear evidence of this.

Training school/Juvenile development center/Juvenile village/Juvenile correction center/Juvenile treatment center/Juvenile service center/School or home for boys and girls—The typical training school may provide supervision, programs, and residential services for more than 100 residents; however, programs of this size are not encouraged. (Standards for new facilities require that each new training school have no more than 100 beds and be limited to two stories in height.) These facilities are designed and operated to be secure institutions.

Juvenile development centers, juvenile treatment centers, secure training schools, and other facilities in the category may serve relatively smaller populations ranging from 40 to 100 juveniles. The age range served is generally from thirteen to eighteen, although in many jurisdictions, residents may be as young as ten or as old as twenty. Older residents are usually juveniles who have been returned to the facility as parole violators.

Treatment plan—A series of written statements that specify the particular course of therapy and the roles of medical and nonmedical personnel in carrying it out. A treatment plan is individualized, based on assessment of the individual patient's needs, and includes a statement of the short- and long-term goals and the methods by which the goals will be pursued. When clinically indicated, the treatment plan provides inmates with access to a range of supportive and rehabilitative services, such as individual or group counseling and/or self-help groups that the physician deems appropriate.

Triage—The screening and classification of offender health care concerns to determine the priority of need and the appropriate level of intervention.

Uncontrolled—Significant clinical signs outside of normal parameters as defined by the responsible physician.

Unit management—A management system that subdivides an institution into units. The unit management system has several basic requirements:

1. Each unit holds a relatively small number of inmates. Ideally, there should be fewer than 150 but not more than 500 inmates.

2. Inmates are housed in the same unit for a major portion of their confinement.

3. Inmates assigned to a unit work in a close relationship with a multidisciplinary staff team who are regularly assigned to the unit and whose officers are located within the unit.

4. Staff members have decision-making authority for the institutional programming and living conditions for the inmates assigned to the unit within broad rules, policies, and guidelines established by the agency and/or the facility administrator.

5. Inmate assignments to a unit are based on the inmate's need for control, security, and programs offered.

Unit management increases contact between staff and inmates, fosters increased interpersonal relationships, and leads to more knowledgeable decision making as a direct result of staff dealing with a smaller, more permanent group. At the same time, the facility benefits from the economies inherent in centralized service facilities, such as utilities, food service, health care, educational systems, vocational programs, and recreational facilities.

Urine surveillance program—A program whereby urine samples are collected on an irregular basis from offenders suspected of having a history of drug use to determine current or recent use.

Volunteer—An individual who donates his or her time and effort to enhance the activities and programs of the agency. They are selected on the basis of their skills or personal qualities to provide services in recreation, counseling, education, religion, and so forth.

Waiver—A commission panel decision that releases the correctional unit from the responsibility of preparing a plan of action to bring the unit into compliance with a standard.

Warden/Superintendent—The individual in charge of the institution; the chief executive or administrative officer. This position is sometimes referred to by other titles, but "warden" and "superintendent" are the most commonly used terms.

Work release—A formal arrangement sanctioned by law whereby an inmate/resident is released into the community to maintain approved and regular employment.

Workers' compensation—A statewide system of benefits for employees who are disabled by job-related injury.

Youthful offender—A person under the age of criminal majority in the jurisdiction in which he or she is confined.

The First Congress of Correction

The 1870 declaration of principles republished on the following pages was passed by the first Congress of Correction after a three-day discussion of the issues and a thorough review of papers presented by delegates from England, Ireland, Italy, France, and Germany. These principles were discussed and enacted to become the original foundation for ACA standards as we know them today. A total of 329 representatives attended that first Congress from 25 states and Canada. True to the intentions that prevailed during that first Congress, ACA standards have been regularly revised to reflect societal changes as they have occurred. All corrections professionals are indebted to these men and women of vision who, for the first time in recorded history, considered worldwide prison conditions and established the first international prison association that was destined to become the American Correctional Association.

Robert Verdeyen
Director, Standards and Accreditation
American Correctional Association

First Congress of Correction Participants

President: His Excellency Rutherford B. Hayes, Governor of Ohio
Vice Presidents:

United States	Rev. E. C. Wines, D.D. LL.D.
Connecticut	E. W. Hatch, M. D.
Indiana	Gov. Conrad Baker
Kansas	Hon. E. Hensley
Maine	Hon. E. G. Harlow
Massachusetts	F. B. Sanborn
Missouri	Rev. D. A. Wilson
New Hampshire	Ex-Gov. Frederick Smyth
New York	Gen Amos Pilsbury
Ohio	Hon. Charles Thomas
Rhode Island	E. M. Snow, M. D.
Wisconsin	Hon. Edwin Hurlbut
California	Rev. James Woodworth
Illinois	George W. Perkins
Iowa	Martin Heisey
Kentucky	Hon. R. K. White
Maryland	G. S. Griffith
Michigan	Hon. C. J. Walker
Nebraska	Hon. F. Templin
New Jersey	Ex-Gov. Daniel Haines
North Carolina	Hon. G. William Welker
Pennsylvania	T. H. Nevin
West Virginia	William B. Curtis, M.D.
Dominion of Canada	William Elder, A. M.
Columbia, South America	Enrique Cortes

Secretaries:

Bradford K. Pierce, D.D., New York
Z. R. Brockway, Michigan
Rev. A. G. Byers, Ohio
Rev. Joshua Coit, Massachusetts

Treasurer:

Charles F. Coffin, Indiana

Guest Presenters to the Congress:

Frederick Merrick, D. D., President of Wesleyan University, Delaware, Ohio
Florence Nightingale, London, England
S. G. Howe, M. D., President, Massachusetts Board State Charities, Boston
M. Bonneville de Marsangy (the Inventor), Counselor of the Imperial Court
of Paris, France
Renssalaer N. Hayes, Esq., Member, Board of Managers, New York Juvenile Asylum,
New York
Joanna Margaret Hill, Bristol, England
M. Beltrani Scalia, Inspector-General of Prisons in the Kingdom of Italy,
Florence, Italy
Baron Franz Von Holzendorff, LL.D., Professor of Law in the Royal University of
Berlin, Prussia
Terence J. O'Neil, Esq., Inspector of Prisons in Canada, Toronto, Ontario
Fr. Bruun, Inspector of Prisons in Denmark, Copenhagen
Sr Walter Crofton, C.B., Winchester, England
Col. G. Y. W. Henderson, Commissioner of Police, London, England
B. F. Wainwright, Superintendent, House of Refuge, Plainfield, Illinois
Mary Carpenter, Superintendent, Red Lodge Reformatory, Bristol, England

Declaration of Principles

Declaration of Principles Adopted and
Promulgated by the Congress
October 12-18, 1870
Cincinnati, Ohio

I.

Crime is an intentional violation of duties imposed by law, which inflicts an injury upon others. Criminals are persons convicted of crime by competent courts.

II.

The treatment of criminals by society is for the protection of society. But since such treatment is directed to the criminal rather than to the crime, its great object should be his moral regeneration.

III.

The progressive classification of prisoners, based on character and worked on some well-adjusted mark system, should be established in all prisons above the common jail.

IV.

Since hope is a more potent agent than fear, it should be made an ever-present force in the minds of prisoners, by a well-devised and skillfully applied system of rewards for good conduct, industry and attention to learning. Rewards, more than punishments, are essential to every good prison system.

V.

The prisoner's destiny should be placed, measurably, in his own hands; he must be put into circumstances where he will be able, through his own exertions, to continually better his own condition. A regulated self-interest must be brought into play, and made constantly operative.

VI.

The two master forces opposed to the reform of the prison systems of our several states are political appointments, and a consequent instability of administration. Until both are eliminated, the needed reforms are impossible.

VII.

Special training, as well as high qualities of head and heart, is required to make a good prison or reformatory officer. Then only will the administration of public punishment become scientific, uniform and successful, when it is raised to the dignity of a profession, and men are specially trained for it, as they are for other pursuits.

VIII.

Peremptory sentences ought to be replaced by those of indeterminate length. Sentences limited only by satisfactory proof of reformation should be substituted for those measured by mere lapse of time.

IX.

Of all reformatory agencies, religion is first in importance, because most potent in its action upon the human heart and life.

X.

Education is a vital force in the reformation of fallen men and women. Its tendency is to quicken the intellect, inspire self-respect, excite to higher aims and afford a healthful substitute of low and vicious amusements. Education is, therefore, a matter of primary importance in prisons, and should be carried to the utmost extent consistent with the other purposes of such institutions.

XI.

In order to the reformation of imprisoned criminals, there must be not only a sincere desire and intention to that end, but a serious conviction, in the minds of the prison officers, that they are capable of being reformed, since no man can heartily maintain a discipline at war with his inward beliefs; no man can earnestly strive to accomplish what in his heart he despairs of accomplishing.

XII.

A system of prison discipline, to be truly reformatory, must gain the will of the convict. He is to be amended; but how is this possible with his mind in a state of hostility? No system can hope to succeed, which does not secure this harmony of wills, so that the prisoner shall choose for himself what his officer chooses for him. But, to this end, the officer must really choose the good of the prisoner, and the prisoner must remain in his choice long enough for virtue to become a habit. This consent of wills is an essential condition of reformation.

XIII.

The interest of society and the interest of the convicted criminal are really identical, and they should be made practically so. At present there is a combat between crime and laws. Each sets the other at defiance and, as a rule, there is little kindly feeling, and few friendly acts, on either side.

XIV.

The prisoner's self-respect should be cultivated to the utmost, and every effort made to give back to him his manhood. There is no greater mistake in the whole compass of penal discipline, than its studied imposition of degradation as a part of punishment. Such imposition destroys every better impulse and aspiration. It crushes the weak, irritates the strong, and indisposes all to submission and reform. It is trampling where we ought to raise, and is therefore as unchristian in principle as it is unwise in policy.

XV.

In prison administration, moral forces should be relied upon, with as little admixture of physical force as possible, and organized persuasion be made to take the place of coercive restraint, the object being to make upright and industrious freemen, rather than orderly and obedient prisoners. Brute force may make good prisoners; moral training alone will make good citizens. To the latter of these ends, the living soul must be won; to the former, only the inert and obedient body.

XVI.

Industrial training should have both a higher development and a greater breadth than has heretofore been, or is now, commonly given to it in our prisons. Work is no less an auxiliary to virtue, than it is a means of support. Steady, active, honorable labor is the basis of all reformatory discipline. It not only aids reformation, but is essential to it. It was a maxim with Howard, "make men diligent, and they will be honest"—a maxim which this congress regards as eminently sound and practical.

XVII.

While industrial labor in prisons is of the highest importance and utility to the convict, and by no means injurious to the laborer outside, we regard the contract system of prison labor, as now commonly practised in our country, as prejudicial alike to discipline, finance, and the reformation of the prisoner, and sometimes injurious to the interest of the free laborer.

XVIII.

The most valuable parts of the Irish prison system–the more strictly penal stage of separate imprisonment, the reformatory stage of progressive classification, and the probationary stage of natural training–are believed to be as applicable to one country as another—to the United States as to Ireland.

XIX.

Prisons, as well as prisoners, should be classified or graded so that there shall be prisons for the untried, for the incorrigible and for other degrees of depraved character, as well as separate establishments for women, and for criminals of the younger class.

XX.

It is the judgement of this congress, that repeated short sentences for minor criminals are worse than useless; that, in fact, they rather stimulate than repress transgression. Reformation is a work of time; and a benevolent regard to the good of the criminal himself, as well as to the protection of society, requires that his sentence be long enough for reformatory processes to take effect.

XXI.

Preventive institutions, such as truant homes, industrial schools, etc., for the reception and treatment of children not yet criminal, but in danger of becoming so, constitute the true field of promise, in which to labor for the repression of crime.

XXII.

More systematic and comprehensive methods should be adopted to save discharged prisoners, by providing them with work and encouraging them to redeem their character and regain their lost position in society. The state has not discharged its whole duty to the criminal when it has punished him, nor even when it has reformed him. Having raised him up, it has the further duty to aid in holding him up. And to this end it is desirable that state societies be formed, which shall cooperate with each other in this work.

XXIII.

The successful prosecution of crime requires the combined action of capital and labor, just as other crafts do. There are two well-defined classes engaged in criminal operations, who may be called the capitalists and the operatives. It is worthy of inquiry, whether a more effective warfare may not be carried on against crime, by striking at the capitalists as a class, than at the operatives one by one. Certainly, this double warfare should be vigorously pushed, since from it the best results, as regards repressive justice, may be reasonably hoped for.

XXIV.

Since personal liberty is the rightful inheritance of every human being, it is the sentiment of this congress that the state which has deprived an innocent citizen of this right, and subjected him to penal restraint, should, on unquestionable proof of its mistake, make reasonable indemnification for such wrongful imprisonment.

XXV.

Criminal lunacy is a question of vital interest to society; and facts show that our laws regarding insanity, in its relation to crime, need revision, in order to bring them to a more complete conformity to the demands of reason, justice and humanity; so that, when insanity is pleaded in bar of conviction, the investigation may be conducted with greater knowledge, dignity and fairness; criminal responsibility be more satisfactorily determined; the punishment of the sane criminal be made more sure, and the restraint of the insane be rendered at once more certain and more humane.

XXVI.

While this congress would not shield the convicted criminal from the just responsibility of his misdeeds, it arraigns society itself as in no slight degree accountable for the invasion of its rights and the warfare upon its interests, practised by the criminal classes. Does society take all the steps which it easily might, to change, or at least to improve, the circumstances in our social state that lead to crime; or, when crime has been committed, to cure the proclivity to it, generated by these circumstances? It cannot be pretended. Let society, then, lay the case earnestly to its conscience, and strive to mend in both particulars. Offences, we are told by a high authority, must come; but a special woe is denounced against those through whom they come. Let us take heed that that woe fall not upon our head.

XXVII.

The exercise of executive clemency in the pardon of criminals is a practical question of grave importance, and of great delicacy and difficulty. It is believed that the annual average of executive pardons from the prisons of the whole county reaches ten percent of their population. The effect of the too free use of the pardoning power is to detract from the certainty of punishment for crimes, and to divert the mind of prisoners from the means supplied for their improvement. Pardons should be issue for one or more of the following reasons, viz.: to release the innocent, to correct mistakes made in imposing the sentence, to relieve such suffering from ill-health as requires release from imprisonment, and to facilitate or reward the real reformation of the prisoner. The exercise of this power should be by the executive, and should be guarded by careful examination as to the character of the prisoner and his conduct in prison. Furthermore, it is the opinion of this congress that governors of states should give to their respective legislatures the reasons, in each case, for their exercise of the pardoning power.

XXVIII.

The proper duration of imprisonment for a violation of the laws of society is one of the most perplexing questions in criminal jurisprudence. The present extraordinary inequality of sentences for the same or similar crimes is a source of constant irritation among prisoners, and the discipline of our prisons suffers in consequence. The evil is one for which some remedy should be devised.

XXIX.

Prison statistics, gathered from a wide field and skillfully digested, are essential to an exhibition of the true character and working of our prison systems. The collection, collation and reduction to tabulated forms of such statistics can best be effected through a national prison discipline society, with competent working committees in every state, or by the establishment of a national prison bureau, similar to the recently instituted national bureau of education.

XXX.

Prison architecture is a matter of grave importance. Prisons of every class should be substantial structures, affording gratification by their design and material to a pure taste, but not costly or highly ornate. We are of the opinion that those of moderate size are best, as regards both industrial and reformatory ends.

XXXI.

The construction, organization and management of all prisons should be by the state, and they should form a graduated series of reformatory establishments, being arranged with a view to the industrial employment, intellectual education and moral training of the inmates.

XXXII.

As a general rule, the maintenance of penal institutions, above the county jail, should be from the earnings of the inmates, and without cost to the state; nevertheless, the true standard of merit in their management is the rapidity and thoroughness of reformatory effect accomplished thereby.

XXXIII.

A right application of the principles of sanitary science in the construction and arrangements of prisons is a point of vital importance. The apparatus for heating and ventilation should be the best that is known; sunlight, air and water should be afforded according to the abundance with which nature has provided them; the rations and clothing should be plain but wholesome, comfortable, and in sufficient but not extravagant quantity; the bedsteads, bed and bedding, including sheets and pillowcases, not costly but decent, and kept clean, well aired and free from vermin; the hospital accommodations, medical stores and surgical instruments should be all that humanity requires and science should supply; and all needed means for personal cleanliness should be without stint.

XXXIV.

The principle of the responsibility of parents for the full or partial support of their criminal children in reformatory institutions has been extensively applied in Europe, and its practical working has been attended with the best results. It is worthy of inquiry whether this principle may not be advantageously introduced into the management of our American reformatory institutions.

XXXV.

It is our conviction that one of the most effective agencies in the repression of crime would be the enactment of laws by which the education of all the children of the state should be made obligatory. Better to force education upon the people than to force them into prison to suffer for crimes, of which the neglect of education and consequent ignorance have been the occasion, if not the cause.

XXXVI.

As a principle that crowns all, and is essential to all, it is our conviction that no prison system can be perfect, or even successful to the most desirable degree, without some cental authority to sit at the helm, guiding, controlling, unifying and vitalizing the whole. We ardently hope yet to see all the departments of our preventive, reformatory and penal institutions in each state moulded into one harmonious and effective system; its parts mutually answering to and supporting each other; and the while animated by the same spirit, aiming at the same objects, and subject to the same control; yet without loss of the advantages of voluntary aid and effort, wherever they are attainable.

XXXVII.

This congress is of the opinion that, both in the official administration of such a system, and in the voluntary co-operation of citizens therein, the agency of women may be employed with excellent effect.

Proposal for Standard Revision

ACA File No. _____

This official proposal form is to be used for changes to all ACA standards manuals. Following completion of the proposal form, it will be presented to the Standards Committee at the next meeting. Proposals to be considered after August 1, 1992 must be made in accordance with the following guidelines.

I. **Manual**—Insert the name of each manual to which you believe the changes apply.
II. **Edition**—Insert the edition number(s) of all applicable manuals.
III. **Standard Number(s)**—Insert all numbers that apply to your proposal.
IV. **Agency/Facility**
    A. Size of Facility—State the size of the facility you operate and/or work in.
    B. Size of Agency—State the total size of your agency.
V. **Date of Proposal**

I. Manual	II. Edition

III. Existing Standard Number   IV. Agency/Facility
    A. Size of Facility:
    B. Size of Agency:
	V. Date of Proposal

VI. Type of Proposal (check appropriate box) ☐ New Standard ☐ Revision ☐ Deletion

VII. Exisiting Standard (insert complete standard and existing discussion/comment; a photocopy is preferable)

_____

_____

_____

_____

_____

_____

_____

VIII. Proposal (state the standard and discussion exactly as you believe it should appear in the manual; proposal must be in the same format and worded precisely)

_____

_____

_____

_____

_____

_____

_____

Proposed Discussion/Comment

_____

_____

_____

_____

_____

_____

IX. Impact Statements—It is imperative that all standards be developed after careful consideration of the impact the action will have on staffing, budget, programs, construction, and legal/legislative activities. In each category, state the numbers as exactly as possible, and cite data sources.

A. Staffing

1. On the Facility

_____

_____

_____

_____

2. On the Agency

_____

_____

_____

_____

B. Annual Budget
   1. On the Facility

_____

_____

_____

_____

   2. On the Agency

_____

_____

_____

_____

C. Program

_____

_____

_____

_____

_____

_____

_____

D. Construction (describe the impact your proposal may have on the physical plant)

_____

_____

_____

_____

_____

E. Legal/Legislative

_____

_____

_____

_____

_____

X. **General Comments** (explain in your own words why you believe the action should be taken)

_____

_____

_____

_____

_____

_____

_____

_____

Submitted by (name and title) _____

Signature _____

Agency _____

Address _____

City _____ State _____ Zip _____

Telephone (include area code) _____ FAX _____

Forward to:

American Correctional Association
Standards and Accreditation Department
Attn: Standards Coordinator
206 North Washington Street, Suite 200
Alexandria, VA 22314

Index